# Toward Communication Competency

This book is a companion to **Interplay: The Process of Interpersonal Communication,** Third Edition, by Ronald B. Adler, Lawrence B. Rosenfeld, and Neil Towne.

# Toward Communication Competency

---

## Developing Interpersonal Skills

Second Edition

**Susan R. Glaser**
University of Oregon

**Anna Eblen**
Eastern Montana College

**Holt, Rinehart and Winston**
New York   Chicago   San Francisco   Philadelphia
Montreal   Toronto   London   Sydney
Tokyo   Mexico City   Rio de Janeiro   Madrid

To Peter, Meegan, and Sam
To Rick and Mario

Cover: Pierre Auguste Renoir, <u>Le Moulin de la Galette</u>, 1876, Musée d'Orsay, Paris. Courtesy of Giraudon/Art Resource, N.Y.

**Library of Congress Cataloging-in-Publication Data**

Glaser, Susan R.
   Toward communication competency.

   Bibliography: p.
   Includes index.
   1. Interpersonal communication. I. Eblen, Anna.
II. Title.
HM132.G54   1986       153.6       85–17623
ISBN 0-03-002864-7

CBS COLLEGE PUBLISHING
Holt, Rinehart and Winston
The Dryden Press
Saunders College Publishing

# Preface

Watch a baby learning to talk, and you will realize once again the delight
and frustration we humans experience in our interpersonal communication.
We all know the flash of triumph we feel when a friend shows understanding
of our latest brainstorm. Likewise, we have moaned with disappointment
when our ideas are misunderstood. We have played with interpersonal
communication, perhaps trying out a new conversational style that we have
seen and admired. Our families used the direct approach to remind us of
our manners. ("Say thank you for the nice socks, dear.") All of these
experiences —successes, mistakes, observations, instructions—are ways we
learn interpersonal communication.

In a structured experience like a class, however, we want to apply
theories of interpersonal learning systematically. The ideal experience
combines information and practice. This text provides methods for people to
plan and practice communication improvement.

In life, some of the communication habits we have learned serve us
better than other patterns. It happens that a few of us were lucky or clever
enough to acquire interpersonal skills that need only fine tuning. Others
have skills that served well in past situations, but need adapting to changed
life conditions. Still others haven't had the chance to learn and practice a
certain skill because the need only recently arose. Whatever the case, the
program of instruction in this text will help in a move toward increased
competency in communication. People do not develop effective
communication skills by reading *about* them. You wouldn't expect to learn

to swim, ski, or play tennis merely by reading about these sports. You would probably assume that learning each of these skills would require practice and behavior change.

Understanding theory does not necessarily lead to change. The transfer of learning to daily living does not come automatically. There is a difference between knowing and doing, and merely knowing *about* communication may have little or no impact on what you *do* when you communicate. *Interplay* is designed to teach you about theory and research related to interpersonal communication. *Toward Communication Competency* is intended to help you develop more effective skills in communicating interpersonally.

**To the Student**    Each quarter we stand before an audience of people like you to talk about interpersonal communication. We make a promise to our students at the beginning of our work together, and we make the same promise to you. We say, "If you will learn to observe, plan, and practice any communication you choose, we promise that you can change it." If you make the decision to improve a skill, follow the ideas in this book about your skill, and rehearse the skill, you will improve. At the end of an activity like the skill change project in Chapter 1, you will be able to perform your chosen communication skill in a way that you can only imagine right now. You are challenged and interested by many of your college classes; this class should hold extra fascination because it is all about *you* and what happens in your life. The purpose of this book is to help you influence the interpersonal events in which you participate.

**To the Instructor**    Those of us who have taught even one section of a fundamental interpersonal communication course have probably pondered the question: What is it that we teach, and how can we increase the likelihood that our course will have an impact on the lives of our students outside of our classroom? The focus of this book is on change. The book is specifically designed to involve students in active observation of their communicative lives and to help them select and subsequently implement interpersonal behavior change. Students are provided with activities, assignments, group experiences, and projects that allow them to become more aware of their own communication behaviors and the communication behavior of those with whom they interact. Most importantly, the book teaches students how to observe and modify their own communication in situations of their choice.

Many of the chapters offer more activities and assignments than could possibly be completed within the time constraints of most classes. This was done because not all of the activities will fit into the framework of every course. Therefore we have tried to give you the option to select those most appropriate for you. Whenever possible, the instructional program was based on available research data. We have included a reference section at the conclusion of the book to indicate the sources primarily responsible for the development of each chapter. But because research in the area of interpersonal competency is still so limited, a sizable portion of this book is based on what Susan Glaser has observed and developed during ten years as director of her department's interpersonal program.

We hope you will find this book useful in translating what you teach into student behavior change. We believe this outcome is foremost among our goals as instructors of interpersonal communication.

## Acknowledgments

Several segments of this book have been adapted or taken directly from Glaser and Biglan's *Increase Your Confidence and Skill in Interpersonal Situations*, a social skills manual. Susan R. Glaser would like to thank her coauthor, Anthony Biglan, for agreeing to the inclusion of those sections in this work. The Glaser and Biglan program was developed and evaluated over a two-year period at the University of Oregon, and reports of this research are currently available. We also express our thanks to Peter A. Glaser, who developed the role plays in this book.

We would also like to recognize the positive influence of our students at the University of Oregon and Eastern Montana College. Their responses to the first edition of this text gave us direction for this revised version.

Eugene, Oregon                                                          **SRG**
Billings, Montana                                                         **AE**

# Contents

# 1 Interpersonal Process

When we seek to observe and improve our own communication, one basic task is acquiring terminology we can use to describe our experience. Chapter 1 of *Interplay* presents a model of communication in which we act as senders and receivers of messages. This model might also be called an example of an interpersonal *system*. An interpersonal system is a set of people who interrelate to form a unique whole.

Human communication occurs within the context of a system. This means that behavior is difficult to understand or to explain apart from the system within which it has some purpose or function. A communication system may be identified according to the relationship that exists among its members. For example: students and teachers are members of a classroom system; parents and their children are parts of a family system; roommates are participants in a shared living system; lovers are members of a particular intimate system. All of us are members of hundreds of different systems, and each elicits different behaviors from us.

Think for a moment of communicating with your parents. Now think of yourself talking with your roommate or school friends or coworkers. Are you saying and doing the same things? Probably not. Likely, a different part of you emerges in each different system. You may wonder which of these communication roles reveals your "real self." In fact, the real self appears to be a summation of the selves revealed in varying communication systems. Encounters in different communication systems are strung together like beads on a thread of consistency we call the self. Only the whole chain would be called the real self.

Your different communication roles play an important part in your being able to adapt to a large number of systems. You can, for example, transfer listening skills you learn in your classroom system to professional situations in which you listen to a client. It is adaptive, however, for you to modify your communication according to systemic restraints. You would not wish to take the role of candid friend into your first interactions with a new boss. At times you may wish to transfer a skill to a new setting or to acquire a new skill in an ongoing system. Such attempts are commonly resisted by the system.

Systems characteristically maintain a balance among the interrelated people within the group. We all participate actively in achieving this balance when we continue to use the rules, patterns, and norms developed within each system. For example, in the classroom, we usually obey the unwritten rule that students will sit at desks, take notes, and participate at times, while the teacher will lecture. Although this balance is often satisfactory, it is easy to become locked into a pattern of behavior that is too limited within a given system.

Many systems, in fact, seem to pull us into particular interaction patterns. A lot of college students, for example, complain that their parents refuse to treat them as adults. Instead, their parents continue to talk with them as they were at age fourteen or fifteen. In such situations, original interaction patterns have been kept intact long after the participants have grown and changed. Similarly, husbands and wives, or friends and lovers often find themselves repeating unpleasant and undesirable communication patterns. These circumstances happen because changing our own habitual behavior is difficult, and also because other people in our communication systems often resist our attempts to change. If we acknowledge that our communication behavior is partly maintained by the systems in which we participate, we can then achieve the capacity to modify our behavior in line with our goals.

People belong to many systems, which influence how we see the world and how the world sees us. If we begin to analyze our own communication behavior in the context of the system in which it occurs, we can begin to discover how people in our interpersonal systems give positive and negative sanctions to our communication behavior.

---

**Individual Activity**
**Discovering Interpersonal Systems**

1. To what different systems do you belong? List two. _____

_____

_____

**2.** How do these systems reward you? _____

_____

_____

**3.** What communication behaviors are rewarded in each system? _____

_____

_____

**4.** How do these systems punish you? _____

_____

_____

**5.** What communication behaviors meet with negative consequences in each system? _____

_____

_____

Communication systems tend to maintain their balanced state by giving positive and negative consequences for certain kinds of communication behavior. That is, the people in the system reward each other for normative communication and punish each other for inappropriate communication. Consider the example of students answering questions in a classroom setting. They might be rewarded by nods from their classmates or by an affirmation from their teacher. The degree to which an individual in the system decides to participate in normative communication relates to how important and rewarding the system appears. For example, students might decide to spend the evening studying for a favorite class in their major area rather than for a less enjoyable general education requirement.

**Class Discussion**
**Participating in Systems**

**1.** Why is it important to give positive feedback to your friends and acquaintances? Why is it sometimes difficult?

**2.** Why is it sometimes difficult to receive positive feedback from people in a system? Why is it important?

**3.** Why is it important to give negative feedback? Why is it difficult?

**4.** Why is it difficult to receive negative feedback? Why is it important?

Systems must be adaptable if they are to continue to exist in a changing environment. By enrolling in an interpersonal communication class, you have decided to improve the communication environment in your own systems. You have created within yourself a determination that can help your systems to adapt to your new goal. You will meet some resistance as the systems try to maintain the old balance, but your persistence will achieve a new, more pleasing balance. You *can* change communication patterns.

## Changing Communication Behavior within a System

Changing the way you communicate is a challenge. We must learn to observe a behavior that is close to us. In fact, our communication behavior is as much a part of us as the way we walk or the rate of our breathing. Yet changing the way we communicate is entirely possible, and the consequences of such change can be astonishing. So far this book has talked about interpersonal processes. Now the discussion will present strategies for changing your own communication behavior. The remainder of Chapter 1 will help you to choose some opportunities for change in your personal communication. You will monitor your own behavior, formulate some goals, and begin to reach those goals. Then, in subsequent chapters, you will continue to work on these and other communication skills.

*Notice that Chapter 1 presents a behavior change procedure designed for a four to eight week period.* Although each step of the procedure is included in this chapter, you need not complete the project before moving on to the rest of the book. In fact, the remainder of the book will assist you in discovering options, strategies, and alternatives for changing the way you communicate. The authors intend that your instructor will guide you through the stages of this project according to the time constraints of your particular class. You are encouraged to work in ongoing communication skill groups so that you may learn from others about your progress and chances for improvement.

The group experience provides help and information that prove important to a successful change. The group members form an experimental system where you can try out new communication ideas; they give you the positive feedback you'll want as you begin to try communication changes outside the classroom.

Before you can begin a communication skill project, you will need to select a relevant communication behavior to work on. One word of advice: Spend some time choosing your goal. Since you'll be devoting significant time and energy to this particular project, and since it is such a rare opportunity to spend class time working on self improvement, it is worth taking some extra time now to choose a skill that is particularly significant to you and worth this much attention.

**Individual Activity**
**Selecting a Communication Goal**

The following procedure, adapted from Ron Adler's *Confidence in Communication* (1977), will help you select your communication goal. Take some time now to think about problems you have communicating with other people. Then describe these difficulties below.

**Difficulties You Have Communicating with Strangers and Acquaintances.**

EXAMPLE:  I can't start a conversation with someone I've never met before.

EXAMPLE:  I can't ask an acquaintance to do something for me.

1.  I can't _____

2.  I can't _____

3.  I can't _____

**Difficulties You Have Communicating with Friends.**

EXAMPLE:  I can't say "no" when my friends want to borrow my clothes.

EXAMPLE  I can't ask my friends for favors even when I need their help.

1.  I can't _____

2.  I can't _____

3.  I can't _____

## Difficulties You Have Communicating with Family Members.

**EXAMPLE:**    I can't ask my husband to do more childcare.

**EXAMPLE:**    I can't discipline my daughter without becoming angry.

**1.**   I can't _____

_____

**2.**   I can't _____

_____

**3.**   I can't _____

_____

## Difficulties You Have Communicating with People at School or at Work.

**EXAMPLE:**    I can't say "no" when my boss asks me to work overtime.

**EXAMPLE:**    I can't participate in class discussions even when I know the answers or have a question.

**1.**   I can't _____

_____

**2.**   I can't _____

_____

**3.**   I can't _____

_____

When you have completed your list, read each item out loud. When finished, read the list again, but this time substitute the word "won't" for "can't." For example, "I can't ask my husband to do more childcare" becomes "I won't ask my husband to do more childcare." Were there difficulties on your list for which the word "won't" seemed more accurate than the word "can't"? Probably so, for there are very few communication behaviors which people are physically unable to do. "Won't" suggests that an element of choice is involved. Usually, this choice is not based on feeling good about what you're doing, but rather on a lack of knowledge about how to perform more effectively. To test this hypothesis, review your list one final time, now substituting "I don't know" for your original "can't." Instead of saying, "I can't say no when my friends want to borrow my clothes" try, "I don't know how to say 'no'." The "don't know how to" items on your list are the ones to consider for the communication skill project. These are the ones you can expect to change by reading this book.

To obtain some further ideas for communication goals, refer to the following list of skills frequently chosen by students in the past. This list is certainly not exhaustive. It was adapted from a similar project developed by Paul Freedman at the University of Kansas.

## Initiating Interaction, Widening the Scope of Your Interaction

1. Meet and get to know people; overcome shyness; begin new relationships.

2. Relate to people from different social, religious, racial, political, age, or educational groups.

3. Relate to members of the opposite sex.

4. Make conversation or small talk in informal social situations or with strangers.

## Asserting Yourself

5. Initiate ideas and actions forcefully; give orders or instructions when the situation calls for you to do so.

6. Assert yourself when you are right; argue well; logically defend your point of view.

7. Say "no" to requests, offers, dates, or salespeople.

8. Ask for a favor, a date, a loan, or inclusion in a group, or for information about ideas, techniques, or personal matters of other people.

9. Be independent; differ from others in a group; refuse to conform or go along.

10. Complain about bad treatment; rebel against an injustice; speak up about prejudice, rudeness, unfairness.

## Managing Interaction

11. Give and receive compliments; express and receive warmth or friendliness; show caring, admiration, or love.

12. Keep conversations going; listen actively; manage interruptions; end conversations comfortably when you want to.

13. When you disagree or when someone's comments make you uncomfortable, express your feelings in a manner that does not damage your relationship.

14. Compromise in a dignified way; avoid dominating a conversation; resist the temptation to take control or interrupt; allow others to disagree amiably with you.

## Part A: Monitoring Your Communication Skill

For the next two weeks, observe your behavior and keep a daily journal. Every time you actually do the communication behavior, or want to do the behavior, record the incident in your journal. Record the incident soon after it occurs. Do not try to change the communication, *just record what usually happens,* both good and bad examples. To help you monitor, set up your journal in the following way:

\*\*My general skill is to be more independent; differ from others in a group; refuse to conform.

| Specific Situation | Specific Behavior | Preferred Behavior |
|---|---|---|
| This column should briefly give the date/time of day/place/others present (the basic data). | This column should describe the specific behaviors you manifested during the situation. What did you do when you attempted your communications skill? What did you say? | This column should describe what you would have preferred to say or do in the situation described. |
| **MONITORING EXAMPLE:** | | |
| 9/26 Marylou came into my apt. at 9 pm—I was in my bedroom. She wanted me to go to Duffy's. | Although I did not want to go I said "yeah." I did not look at her. I stayed on my bed and said, "I really should not go because I really need to get some rest." Marylou told me I should get out and meet people. I couldn't think of anything else to say, so I went with her. | I would rather have said, "You're right. I really should get out to meet people, and I'd like to go tomorrow; but tonight I feel tired and want to get some rest." |

| Specific Situation | Specific Behavior | Preferred Behavior |
|---|---|---|
|  |  |  |

| Specific Situation | Specific Behavior | Preferred Behavior |
| --- | --- | --- |
|  |  |  |

## Part B: Describing Communication Patterns

After you have monitored your communication skill for about ten days, review your entries and look for patterns. Where, when, and with whom did you perform your skill most effectively? Least effectively? The following questions can help you locate patterns:

**1.** At what time did you perform your skill most effectively? Least effectively?

**2.** In what places? With what people?

**3.** What other recurring communication behaviors did you manifest when you did or did not perform your skill?

Remember, these patterns should come from the monitoring data you recorded on the blank pages, provided for this purpose. When you make a statement about an observed pattern, be sure to document it with specific data from your monitoring.

### EXAMPLE PATTERNS:

**1.** I say "no" most effectively with my children when they ask for junk food. In these situations I give a firm "no" without hesitation or excuses.
Specific monitoring data that indicate this pattern: 9/26, 9/28, 10/1.

**2.** I perform my skill least effectively with my husband and close friends. When my friends or husband ask me to do something I don't want to do, I usually begin by saying "no," but then, if they try to change my mind, I usually feel guilty and then give in.
Specific monitoring data that indicate this pattern: 9/18, 9/20, 9/21. I

**3.** When I say "no" ineffectively, I often do the following:
  **a.** Make excuses—"I'd really like to drive you to the store, but I have to start dinner." In this case, I didn't really want to drive to the store and I didn't have to start dinner.
  Specific monitoring data that indicate this pattern: 9/19, 9/22.

  **b.** I often begin my "no saying" with phrases such as: "Oh, I don't know"; "I really shouldn't"; "It sounds nice, but." These phrases seem to urge others to persuade me out of my position.
  Specific monitoring data that indicate this pattern: 9/23, 9/24, 9/26, 9/28, 9/30.

**Pattern 1:** _____

_____

_____

**Specific Monitoring Data That Indicate This Pattern:** _____

**Pattern 2:** _____

_____

_____

**Specific Monitoring Data That Indicate This Pattern:** _____

**Pattern 3:** _____

_____

_____

**Specific Monitoring Data That Indicate This Pattern:** _____

_____

_____

**Pattern 4:** _____

_____

_____

_____

**Specific Monitoring Data That Indicate This Pattern:** _____

_____

**Part C: Learning from
Others' Examples:
What Will It Look Like
When I'm Doing It
Well?**

**Modeling**    *Modeling* means watching other people who perform
effectively. Observing others who can perform the skills we are learning
often provides us with some effective behaviors we can borrow. Choose a
person or several people who perform your skill well. Observe the specific
aspects of their verbal and nonverbal behavior. What do they say? How do
they say it? What behaviors would be useful to incorporate into your own
repertoire? Also, find negative models, people who perform the skill
ineffectively. Watching these can be very useful. What behavior do these
people exhibit that you would like to avoid? Using your skill, observe people
for the next few days. Space is provided for you to record five effective
examples and five ineffective examples of your skill.

## Modeling: Observing and Recording Effective Examples of My Skill

**EXAMPLE:**    My roommate was studying when her friend came in and asked her to go out to dinner. My roommate replied, "It sounds like fun, but I really *must* study tonight." She looked at him directly.

1. _____

_____

_____

2. _____

_____

_____

3. _____

_____

_____

4. _____

_____

_____

5. _____

_____

_____

## Modeling: Observing and Recording Ineffective Examples of My Skill

**EXAMPLE:**    My friend's sister asked to borrow his car. He said, "I wish I could lend it to you but I have to go grocery shopping." When his sister said she would drop him off and pick him up at the supermarket, he just said, "Okay." While he said it, he twisted his ring and shuffled his feet.

1. _____

_____

_____

2. _____

_____

_____

**3.** _____

_____

_____

**4.** _____

_____

_____

**5.** _____

_____

_____

Establishing specific, observable goals is an important aspect of behavior change. When our goals are established in behavioral terms, we know what to aim for, we know when we have succeeded, and we know precisely what to do differently when we do not perform effectively. Statements of goals should begin to emerge from your monitoring and pattern descriptions. Another way to help clarify goals is through modeling. Use the models you have recorded; evaluate their strong and weak points, trying to decide which of their behaviors you would feel comfortable using.

## Part D: Goal Analysis

The communication skill you selected earlier in this project is not stated in specific behavioral terms. For example, "I want to overcome shyness and meet new people" gives you little direction. Some questions you might want to ask yourself are: What new people? Where will I meet them? When will I meet them? How many do I want to meet? How often? What will I say when I meet them? What do I typically do in these situations that I want to avoid? In *Goal Analysis*, Robert Mager (1972) offers a procedure for changing poorly defined, ambiguous goals into specific behavioral performances. Following is a summary of Mager's method for analyzing and specifying goals:

**Step 1**  Write down a goal.

**EXAMPLE:**  Listen Actively.

**Step 2**  Jot down the performances that describe the goal. Do that which seems most relevant or comfortable to you.

**a.**  What must a person be doing for me to say that he or she has achieved the goal?

**EXAMPLE:**  Must nod and use intermittent eye contact.

**b.**   Given a room full of people, what is the basis on which I will separate them into two classes: those who have achieved the goal and those who have not?

**EXAMPLE:**   Those who have, sit quietly while I speak; those who haven't, fidget and doodle while I'm talking.

**c.**   How will I recognize goal achievement when I see it?

**EXAMPLE:**   I'll see people who reflect the nonverbal expressions of their partners; that is, they smile if their partner tells a funny story. They will ask questions like "So then what happened?"

**d.**   Think of someone who does *not* represent the goal. What does this person say or do?

**EXAMPLE:**   This person gets up and walks around the room while I'm talking.

**Step 3**   Go back over the list and tighten it up. Cross out duplications. Carry out Steps 1 and 2 on any remaining ambiguous terms.

**Step 4**   Describe each important performance. Do this in a statement that identifies the manner (or extent) of the performance you require to be satisfied the goal is achieved.

**EXAMPLE:**   I want to listen actively to my roommate's stories; I will sit down with her, face-to-face, and use eye contact for a few seconds at least twice a minute. I will ask her questions about the content of her story.

**Step 5**   Modify these statements until you can answer "yes" to this question: If someone performed the behaviors I have outlined, would I be willing to say that person had achieved the goal?

**EXAMPLE:**   When my roommate comes in on Saturday night and begins to tell me about her date, I will put down what I am doing and sit down near her, facing in her direction. While she is talking, I will glance at her several times (6 times a minute). If she is telling a funny story, I will smile and nod. I will ask questions to encourage her to talk; I might say "So then what happened?"

Now state your communication goals as specific behavioral performances:

1. _____
_____

2. _____
_____

3. _____

4. _____

## A Program for Behavior Change

Now that you have carefully monitored your communication and designed a specific goal, you are ready to actually begin changing your behavior. We can view this procedure as a shaping process, beginning with small approximations of your goal behavior and concluding with the actual implementation of your goal in the real situation. You will notice that the behavior change procedures described in this chapter are used throughout the rest of the book. The reason for this is that we are focusing our attention on those methods proven effective in controlled research.

**Covert Rehearsal: Practicing in Your Imagination**   *Covert rehearsal* (or imaginal practice) is an effective way of trying out new communication behaviors. As you imagine yourself practicing your new skill, focus hard on specific interactions. Actually think about dialogue—what you say, and how the other person responds. Don't just go through the motions. Really see yourself asking specific questions, making specific comments, and hearing the other person replying. As you imagine the sequence, practice precisely what you want to say and how you want to say it. Experiment with what feels to be the most effective and comfortable way.

By covertly rehearsing in this manner, you make it much more likely that you will be actually performing the behavior comfortably and effectively in real life situations. This surprising effect of covert rehearsal has been shown in numerous recent studies. What makes covert rehearsal particularly useful is that you can carry it around and do it anywhere—in the shower, walking to school, riding on a bus, washing the dishes. The more you vary covertly rehearsing a particular episode, the more likely you will be to perform well in the actual situation. For example, if you're planning to initiate and maintain a conversation with your neighbor, you should think through a number of possible topics and questions before finally choosing what you perceive to be the best.

Covert rehearsal can be used both to prepare for an upcoming communication event, and to evaluate and revise an event that has already occurred. Both of these increase the probability that you will perform your new skill effectively. Note that some people initially find it difficult to imagine specific conversations with others. Keep with it if you have difficulty. You will eventually succeed with practice, and when you do, you will be amazed at the effect.

---

### Part E: Covert Rehearsal: Some Practice

Choose a communication event that you would like to prepare for covertly. Then, in a quiet place, begin thinking about the conversation as you'd like to see it evolve. When you hit rough spots, try a variety of options until you find a response that pleases you. When you're satisfied with your imagined scene, describe it below in script form.

**EXAMPLE:**

I say:   (looking at people at table, smiling) "Hi, may I join you?"

Other says:   "Sure. Sit down."

I say:   (glancing at books on table) "I see you're taking Interpersonal. I have it, too. Who's your prof?"

Other says:   "Glaser. She's great. Who's yours?"

I say: _____

_____

Other says: _____

_____

I say: _____

_____

Other says: _____

_____

I say: _____

_____

Other says: _____

_____

I say: _____

_____

Other says: _____

_____

I say: _____

_____

Other says: _____

_____

I say: _____

_____

Other says: _____

_____

I say: _____

_____

Other says: _____

_____

I say: _____

_____

Other says: _____

_____

I say: _____

_____

Other says: _____

_____

I say: _____

_____

Other says: _____

_____

**Part F: Behavior Rehearsal: Practicing Your New Skill**    Behavior rehearsal is also known as "role playing." This text favors the term *behavior rehearsal* because it suggests that an individual is not playing the role of someone else but rather is rehearsing his or her own behavior. Rehearsing communication behavior is useful both before and after an event. Practicing *before* an event allows you to enter a communication situation in your most prepared state. Rehearsing a disappointing situation *after* it occurs gives you a chance to discover and remedy aspects of your own behavior that were less than satisfactory.

If your instructor has placed you in ongoing communication skill groups, your behavior rehearsal assignment should be carried out there. If not, small classroom groups of five to six people can be formed for this purpose. Working with a friend outside of class is another possibility. Small groups are advocated for this activity because that format provides each participant with a substantial amount of observer input.

**Part G: Actual Implementation: Performing Your Skill in Real Life Situations**  Without your actually implementing your new skill in real life situations, this entire course is nothing more than a theoretical exercise. You should be satisfied with nothing less than real change in real situations, which means that you will need to choose and plan specific situations in which you want to use your new skill. Plan particular times, places, and people with whom to try your new behavior. Of course when an unplanned opportunity arises, you obviously should use it. The important thing is for you to get into the pattern of planning your communication behavior.

Almost any behavior can be planned: compliments, questions, agreement statements, or requests. The more frequently you plan communication behavior, the more skilled you will become at managing what you do and at having an impact on the systems in which you participate. Remember to evaluate your performance each time you attempt your new behavior in actual situations. What seemed to work for you? What did not seem to work? In what situations were you most successful? What behaviors would you like to perform again? What will you do differently the next time?

An important part of changing your communication behavior in real life settings is providing yourself with a reward when you achieve your goal. Part of your reward, if you are working with a small group, will be the recognition your group gives you for your achievement. In addition to social approval, however, you might think of special presents to yourself that will be contingent upon your performance of your new skill.

Begin by making a brief list of gifts or activities that give you pleasure. Many people list such pastimes as listening to music or going to a movie. Find one or two items on your list that you like best; whenever you do your new communication well, reward yourself by doing the pastime or giving yourself a prize. Continue these rewards for several weeks.

Be sure to record your progress. Records can be kept in a number of ways. You might maintain a journal in which you describe each occurrence of your target behavior. Students have also found it useful to use a progress graph. A graph can be a clear, visual representation of the movement you are making. Suppose, for a moment, that you are trying to increase your frequency of compliments to other people. Your record of progress might resemble the graph shown on page 20.

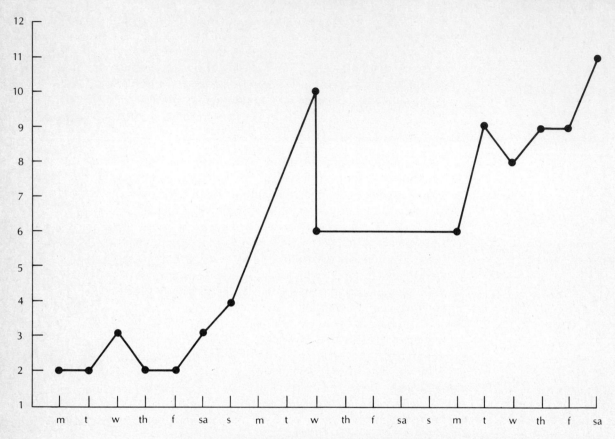

If you choose the graph method to record your progress, be sure to include at least seven days of baseline data before you begin to consciously increase your target behavior. This technique will give you a clearer picture of the movement you are making.

As you proceed with this project be prepared for potential problems. You may reach periodic plateaus in which you are not changing so dramatically as you would like. You may discover that your goal statement is not accurate and that you were trying to increase the wrong behaviors. You may also find that by merely monitoring the frequency of your goal behavior, your rate increases and your problem disappears. In any case, remain flexible and keep working. Revise your goal statement, change your target behavior, promise yourself a special prize for reaching some frequency goal. You're never locked into anything with this project. The goal is behavior change, and there are many avenues for achieving and maintaining that change.

This chapter has explored the systemic nature of communication behavior and has offered a model for behavior change. The remainder of this book will apply these and other procedures to a variety of communication behaviors. When you complete this book you should be able to observe some real differences in your own behavior. Bringing these changes about will require active involvement and effort on your part. You will find that change is directly related to the amount of time you spend working on each new behavior. You have probably heard that many times before but, in this case, the potential for positive consequences is great.

# 2 Self-Concept

What is the image you have of yourself, and how do you feel about this image? Your private set of perceptions about your physical features, thoughts, actions, and feelings represents your *self-concept*. Even though you are the only person to have direct access to your private world, your self-concept affects and is affected by communication.

Your self-concept grows out of a combination of inherited characteristics and social responses to these constitutional differences. For example, a bright child's early talking brings communication from parents and is influenced by the way the parents communicate back. If the parents smile and encourage verbalization by statements like "Good. Say 'big bear' for Uncle, " the child will be more likely to continue talking and incorporate the positive evaluation into a developing self-concept.

When you complete Chapter 2, you should understand how the private world of self-concept develops, how it is maintained, and how communication relates to the evolution of the self-concept. You will have a clearer description of the thoughts, feelings, and perceptions that form your present self-concept. Finally, you will have some ideas about how to build a more positive self-concept, which will facilitate effective communication.

Let's begin by working through some exercises that will give you a clearer picture of the kinds of thoughts, attitudes, and feelings that go into your concept of yourself.

**Individual Activity**
**Who Do You Think You Are?***

For each category below supply the three words or phrases that describe you best.
1.  What moods or feelings best characterize you? (cheerful, considerate, optimistic, etc.)

   a.  _____

   b.  _____

   c.  _____

2.  How would you describe your physical condition and/or your appearance? (tall, attractive, weak, muscular, etc.)

   a.  _____

   b.  _____

   c.  _____

3.  How would you describe your social traits? (friendly, shy, aloof, talkative, etc.)

   a.  _____

   b.  _____

   c.  _____

4.  What talents do you possess or lack? (good artist, lousy carpenter, competent swimmer, etc.)

   a.  _____

   b.  _____

   c.  _____

5.  How would you describe your intellectual capacity? (curious, poor reader, good mathematician, etc.)

   a.  _____

   b.  _____

   c.  _____

6.  What beliefs do you hold strongly? (vegetarian, Christian, pacifist, etc.)

   a.  _____

   b.  _____

   c.  _____

*From  Ronald B. Adler and Neil Towne, *Looking Out/Looking In,* 4th ed., p.37.

**7.** What social roles are the most important in your life? (brother, student, friend, bank teller, club president, etc.)

    **a.** _____

    **b.** _____

    **c.** _____

**8.** What other terms haven't you listed so far that describe other important things about you?

    **a.** _____

    **b.** _____

    **c.** _____

**Individual Activity**
**Discovering My Perceived Self and Ideal Self**

Following you will find two identical lists of twenty-four items. Some of the words or phrases probably describe you quite well, whereas others may not fit you at all. Begin by cutting the first list into cards. Next, place the cards in two piles. One pile should contain those words that describe you best. The other should contain those words that least characterize you. Now repeat the process with the second list, this time organizing the items according to the way you would *like to be*, so that you have a picture of your ideal self when you are finished.

When you have completed this assignment you should have four piles. Two will be descriptions of those items that are most and least characteristic of the way you see yourself now. The other two piles will be those representing items that are most and least characteristic of the way you would like to see yourself. When you have finished this assignment you will have a clearer picture of some aspects of your self that you would like to maintain, as well as some specific areas that you would like to change.

| 1. intelligent | 2. too shy | 3. give in easily |
|---|---|---|
| 4. like other people | 5. feel insecure | 6. talk too much |
| 7. tense | 8. likeable | 9. open-minded |
| 10. confused | 11. friendly | 12. emotionally mature |
| 13. grow in wisdom over time | 14. attractive | 15. selfish |
| 16. afraid to disagree | 17. unreliable | 18. stand up for my personal rights |
| 19. honest with myself | 20. honest with others | 21. make lots of excuses |
| 22. avoid facing things | 23. good student and/or worker | 24. conscientious |

| | | |
|---|---|---|
| **1.** intelligent | **2.** too shy | **3.** give in easily |
| **4.** like other people | **5.** feel insecure | **6.** talk too much |
| **7.** tense | **8.** likeable | **9.** open-minded |
| **10.** confused | **11.** friendly | **12.** emotionally mature |
| **13.** grow in wisdom over time | **14.** attractive | **15.** selfish |
| **16.** afraid to disagree | **17.** unreliable | **18.** stand up for my personal rights |
| **19.** honest with myself | **20.** honest with others | **21.** make lots of excuses |
| **22.** avoid facing things | **23.** good student and/or worker | **24.** conscientious |

You may wonder how this private world developed. To answer this question, we must examine not just your inherent characteristics, but also how people have responded to you, particularly people G. H. Mead (1934) calls "significant others. " These are the people you value and whose approval you seek. Whether parents, friends, teachers, bosses, lovers, or others, they have a tremendous impact on your evolving self-concept.

---

**Individual Activity**
**Your Significant Others**

The following exercise is designed to help you discover some of the central people in the development of your self-concept. A few of these people will have influenced you when you were younger, and others will probably be currently in your life. Think of five such *significant others* whose perceptions of you and responses to you have influenced the way you see yourself. Write the names of these people in the spaces provided, along with the relationship of each to you. Then, under each name, fill in the "I am" statements that you developed as a result of your interactions with this person. For each statement, describe what the person said or did to give you this perception of yourself.

**EXAMPLE:**

**Significant Other:**  My mother

**Told Me I Am:**  Responsible                                    by: saying "I guess you know what you're

doing" when we disagree about a course of action

**Told Me I Am:**  Lovable                                         by: kissing and hugging me and saying,

"I love you"

**Told Me I Am:**  Humorous                                       by: laughing when I tried to be funny

**Told Me I Am:**  Intelligent                                     by: asking me questions about my work

and looking at me when I speak

**Told Me I Am:**  Clumsy                                          by: saying I was never good in athletics

**Significant Other:**  _____

**Told Me I Am:**  _____    by: _____

**Told Me I Am:**  _____    by: _____

**Significant Other:** _____

**Told Me I Am:** _____ by: _____

_____

**Told Me I Am:** _____ by: _____

_____

**Told Me I Am:** _____ by: _____

_____

**Told Me I Am:** _____ by: _____

_____

**Told Me I Am:** _____ by: _____

_____


**Significant Other:** _____

**Told Me I Am:** _____ by: _____

_____

**Told Me I Am:** _____ by: _____

_____

**Told Me I Am:** _____ by: _____

_____

**Told Me I Am:** _____ by: _____

_____

**Told Me I Am:** _____ by: _____

_____


**Significant Other:** _____

**Told Me I Am:** _____ by: _____

_____

**Told Me I Am:** _____ by: _____

_____

**Told Me I Am:** _____ by: _____

_____

Some aspects of your self-concept develop through intrapersonal communication, communication within yourself. Influential cognitive processes include memory, creative problem solving, daydreaming, self-talk, and dreaming. You have no doubt used these internal events as sources of ideas about yourself as well as the world around you.

**Individual Activity**
**Intrapersonal Journal**

Try keeping track of the internal events which reflect your self-concept for the next few days or weeks. By recording a variety of internal events as well as biographical material each day, you will be interested to find how internal and external events interact in the development of self-concept.

| Biographical Notes | Daydreams | Dreams | Other Internal Events |
|---|---|---|---|
|  |  |  |  |

| Biographical Notes | Daydreams | Dreams | Other Internal Events |
|---|---|---|---|
| | | | |

## Individual Activity
## Maintaining Your Self-Concept

Once your self-concept is established, ongoing events and your interpretation of those events help to perpetuate that image. You can recognize how this process operates in your own life by trying the following exercise.

**1.** Review the activities you have completed so far in this chapter, noticing all the labels you have identified as being part of your self-concept. From this group of labels, select the five terms that you believe are the most fundamental descriptions of who you are. Write each term in the appropriate space in the forms provided.

**2.** Use the spaces below each term to record those events occurring within the past week that have helped to reinforce these parts of your self-concept.

**3.** Use the area adjacent to the events you record to identify the thoughts about yourself; that is, those thoughts that accompanied each experience and that led to its affecting your self-concept.

**EXAMPLE:**

**Label:**    Shy

| Event | Self-Talk/Thoughts |
|---|---|
| **Day 1:**   I'm sitting in my English class beside a guy whom I've sat next to all term. I can't think of anything to say, so I say nothing. | I'm such a dud. Why do I have to be so shy? I know he thinks I'm a real loser. |
| **Day 2:**   My friend takes me to a party, and she's the only one I know there. I sit alone all evening since no one comes over to talk to me. My friend is the only one I talk to the whole night. | I can't believe I'm sitting here and having such a terrible time. I knew I should never have come. Nobody wants to talk to me and even if they did, I probably couldn't think of anything to say. |
| **Day 3:**   I went on a "blind date" with a guy who seemed nice enough. I really wanted him to like me, but all I could think of to talk about was school and my hometown. There were a lot of silences. | I'm so nervous and I sound so stupid. I wish I could think of something to say. No wonder I always have to be fixed up on blind dates. |

**EXAMPLE:**

**Label:** _____

| Event | Self-Talk/Thoughts |
|---|---|
| **Day 1:** | |
| **Day 2:** | |
| **Day 3:** | |

**EXAMPLE:**

**Label:** _____

| Event | Self-Talk/Thoughts |
|-------|--------------------|
| **Day 1:** | |
| **Day 2:** | |
| **Day 3:** | |

**EXAMPLE:**

**Label:** _____

| Event | Self-Talk/Thoughts |
|---|---|
| **Day 1:** | |
| **Day 2:** | |
| **Day 3:** | |

**Individual Activity**
**Self-Concept: Behavioral Aspects**

The labels we use to describe ourselves are often based on our behaviors, although we may be unable to identify these actions. You can help pinpoint behavioral aspects of your self-concept by completing the following five "I am" statements with words or phrases that represent components of your self-concept. For this part of the activity you may use any of the lists that you have already made. After you have completed the five "I am" statements, describe the actions that form the basis of your self-description. You should probably observe your actual behavior for two or three days before completing this assignment.

**EXAMPLE:**

**I am:**   assertive

**I do:**   say "no" when people ask me to do things I don't want to do.

**For instance:**   When Jack asked to borrow my car yesterday I told him I didn't want to lend it.

**I do:**   express my feelings to people when I feel good about something they've done or when something they've done disturbs me.

**For instance:**   Yesterday I said to my roommate, "I'm having a hard time studying with your stereo playing. Would you turn it down or off for an hour? Then I'll be finished."

**I do:**   initiate contact with people I'd like to get to know better.

**For instance:**   After my history class on Friday, I asked Georgia if she wanted to go for some coffee. We had a great time.

**1.**   I am: _____

   **a.**   I do: _____

   _____

   For instance: _____

   _____

   **b.**   I do: _____

   _____

   For instance: _____

   _____

   **c.**   I do: _____

   _____

   For instance: _____

   _____

**2.** I am: _____

    **a.**  I do: _____

    _____

    For instance: _____

    _____

    **b.**  I do: _____

    _____

    For instance: _____

    _____

    **c.**  I do: _____

    _____

    For instance: _____

    _____

**3.** I am: _____

    **a.**  I do: _____

    _____

    For instance: _____

    _____

    **b.**  I do: _____

    _____

    For instance: _____

    _____

    **c.**  I do: _____

    _____

    For instance: _____

    _____

**4.** I am: _____

    **a.**  I do: _____

    _____

    For instance: _____

    _____

**b.** I do: _____

_____

For instance: _____

_____

**c.** I do: _____

_____

For instance: _____

_____

**5.** I am: _____

    **a.** I do: _____

_____

For instance: _____

_____

    **b.** I do: _____

_____

For instance: _____

_____

    **c.** I do: _____

_____

For instance: _____

_____

## Individual Activity
## Self-Fulfilling Prophecy: Making Your Own Breaks

What role do *self-fulfilling prophecies* play in shaping your communication? Review the twenty-four self-concept elements you cut into cards. Recall any instances in which you thought about yourself in a manner that helped perpetuate these elements. When have you behaved in ways that reinforced your way of thinking about yourself? List three such instances below. For each, include: (1) a description of the event and how you behaved; (2) the expectation you held; and (3) the part of your self-concept that this behavior reinforced. Also, if your prophecy was a negative one, outline some alternate behavior that might have resulted in a more functional outcome.

**EXAMPLE:**

a. **Event/Behavior:** I was recently invited to a party where I didn't know anybody but the host. I sat by myself all evening and didn't talk to other people. I didn't try to meet anyone.

b. **Expectation:** I was sure I would have a terrible time because I see myself as a shy person, unable to meet strangers.

c. **Self-Concept Reinforced:** This behavior reinforced my view of myself as a shy person and poor communicator.

d. **Alternative Behavior:** Looking back I can see that had I introduced myself to one of the people sitting alone, I might have had a more enjoyable time.


**Situation 1**

a. **Event/Behavior:** _____

_____

_____

b. **Expectation:** _____

_____

_____

c. **Self-Concept Reinforced:** _____

_____

_____

d. **Alternative Behavior:** _____

_____

_____

**Situation 2**

a.  **Event/Behavior:** _____

_____

_____

b.  **Expectation:** _____

_____

_____

c.  **Self-Concept Reinforced:** _____

_____

_____

d.  **Alternative Behavior:** _____

_____

_____

---

### Changing Your Self-Concept: Focusing on the Positive

There is no objective way to interpret a communication event. One interpretation might enhance your self-concept, whereas another interpretation of the same event might lower your self-esteem. Take, for example, an objective event such as being asked to a party. A positive interpretation of this event might be: "I guess Cheryl is interested in getting to know me. I'm glad because she seems like the kind of person I'd like to spend time with. " It would also be possible, however, to interpret the event in a manner likely to have negative consequences for the self-concept. A negative interpretation might be: "I'm sure the only reason she asked me is so that I'll help her study for our exam and lend her my notes. I'll go, but as soon as she starts asking me questions about class, I'll tell her what I really think." It's obvious which one of these interpretations is more likely to lead to the heightening of this person's self-concept.

For the next few days keep track of situations you could interpret in ways either favorable or unfavorable to a positive self-concept. For each one, describe both interpretations and then indicate which interpretation is most reasonable. The goal here is not to turn you into a Pollyana, but rather to help you avoid unnecessary self-putdowns.

| Incident | Positive Interpretation | Negative Interpretation | Most Reasonable Interpretation and Why |
|---|---|---|---|
| EXAMPLE: My wife compliments me on the dinner I cooked. | She really likes my cooking and she appreciates the time it took me to get this meal to-gether. | She's only compli-menting me to get me to cook more often. | She probably does like my cooking. After all, it is a good meal. And she must realize how long it took me. |
| EXAMPLE: | | | |
| EXAMPLE: | | | |
| EXAMPLE: | | | |
| EXAMPLE: | | | |
| EXAMPLE: | | | |

**Self-Concept:
A Preview**

By now you are probably more aware of some of the ways you think about and label yourself. We hope you also understand more clearly the interactive aspects of your self-concept. You have had an opportunity to observe, record, and analyze some of your ongoing interactions and the effect they have on the way you feel about yourself.

People, particularly significant others, have an impact on our self-concept. Undoubtedly, our natural environment and the people in it greatly influence our view of self. Our private environment, however, also influences our self-concepts. An individual's private world and the internal events that only he or she can experience have a large impact on the way one views oneself. This means that when we speak of changing self-concepts, we need to attack the problem on two fronts. This chapter presented ways of viewing that change as it occurs in our public, interactive worlds and began the exploration of how private events influence the development and maintenance of our self-concepts. In Chapter 9 we will continue to explore how self-concept can be managed, changed, and heightened as we view our private worlds and the private events within them. To repeat a basic orientation of this book: The self-concept and behavior are interactive. Self-concept changes as behavior changes, and adjustments in thoughts about the self will help promote behavioral management.

Years of communication and personal reflection have contributed to the way you see yourself. One chapter in one book can only *begin* to create an awareness of the complexities of the self. Any significant changes in the complicated system of the self usually grow out of a careful program of changing behavior and cognition. For example, if you communicate effectively with a friend, you begin to change the way you see yourself; your personal positive evaluation of the talk will encourage you to try again. Choices you make about changing behavior and your appraisals of this effort can give a new direction to your evolving self-concept.

# 3 Perception

Even when we try to be aware of all the sensory detail in a situation, we cannot. All the stimuli in the interpersonal situation arrive simultaneously, and we create meaning for ourselves as we select and analyze the information. Perception is the process by which we assign meaning to the mass of sensory stimuli.

Often two people participating in the same event perceive it so differently that it seems they could not have been together. Has it ever happened to you? You begin to tell a story to a friend about a place you went together. Your friend says, "No, that's not the way it was, " and tells a completely different version.

We structure our own reality. Not only do we have different abilities and methods for "taking in" sensory data, but also we interpret the data in unique ways. This means that our perceptions, rather than being objective, accurate records of interpersonal events, are really no more than personally structured stories about the event. We use these stories, however, to help us make predictions about future interactions, so that we can make sense of interpersonal situations.

This chapter focuses on some specific communication skills helpful in managing individual differences in perception. You will learn about the sensations that contribute to perception and the physiological factors that affect your interpretation of situations. You will practice alternative methods of dealing with differences in perception and interpretation of interpersonal events. When you complete this chapter you should understand how communication can help resolve perceptual differences. You should also be more skilled at checking out your own perceptions and interpretations.

**Individual Activity**
**Experiencing Sensation and Perception**

Sit quietly. Listen to the sounds around you right now. What do you hear? Focus your attention now on what you can see around you. Look beyond the book you are reading to the room around you. Turn your attention to the feelings within your body; notice how you are sitting, how your clothing feels. Although you were not previously attending to these sensations, all of them are available for perception.

When you selected a set of sensations and interpreted them, you experienced perception. For example, if you organized a set of visual sensations into the concept "window," you *perceived* the window.

___

**Individual Activity**
**Perception: Effect of Physiological Factors**

For the next few days observe the effects of these physiological factors on situational outcomes, and record your observations in the spaces provided.

| Physiological Factors | Situation(s) | Effect of Physiological Factor on Situational Outcome |
|---|---|---|
| Fatigue | **EXAMPLE:**  We prepared dinner for Milke and Donna. Waking up that morning at 4:00 A.M. to go fishing, we were very tired by dinner time. | We didn't do much talking. Particularly, we asked very few questions. This meant that Donna and Milke didn't get to tell us much about themselves. |
| Health | | |
| Fatigue | | |
| Age | | |
| Sex | | |
| Height | | |
| Hunger | | |

**Individual Activity**
**Perception: Social Factors**

Social factors can also influence perception. As a test of this hypothesis try the following survey. Choose one or more statements from the list of survey statements. Then present these statements to people of varying social backgrounds—those of different ages, sex roles, educational levels, political orientations, economic positions, ethnic backgrounds, etc. Ask people to agree or disagree with the statement, explaining their reasons. Does the position on these issues tend to vary systematically as a consequence of the respondent's social background?

**Survey Statements:**

1. Men and women should live together before marrying.

2. The federal government should take control of the oil industry.

3. Abortion should be legalized.

4. The federal government should provide jobs for all unemployed people.

5. Gays should be guaranteed full rights under the law.

_____

_____

_____

_____

_____

**Dyad Activity**
**Perception: Sex Roles**

Imagine that you were born a member of the opposite sex. In your dyad discuss the following questions: Try to think about how your life would have been in your own family, at the time when you were born.

**Infancy**
What is your name?
Describe your environment (your room).
How do your parents and siblings play with you? How do they talk to you?
Who are your caretakers? What are they teaching you?
What toys do you have?
What is your first word? Your first sentence? Why?

**Childhood**
What is your room like now?
What toys and games do you play?
Who are your friends? Who is your best friend?
What kind of clothing do you wear?
What do you and your parents do together?
What TV shows and books do you like?
When you are punished, what did you do to get in trouble?

**Adolescence**
How do you get along with your family?
Who are your best friends? What do you talk about with them? Where do you go?
What do you think about the opposite sex? Do you date? What do you do on dates?
What is your best subject in school? What are your goals?
Do you plan to get married? What do you think about marriage?
Have you ever been in trouble? For what?
What do you do in spare time if you are alone? What are your hobbies and interests?

**Adulthood**
Who are your friends? Did you get married? When?
Do you have children? How many? What are your expectations for their future?
What do you do for money?
What sort of work do you do at home—what are your jobs?
What are your favorite leisure activities? Where do you like to go?
What sort of place do you live in? What rooms are "yours"?
What is your goal for 5 years from now? 20 years?
What will you do when you reach retirement age?
Which of your dreams will remain unfulfilled?
What is the greatest accomplishment of your life?

## Selective Perception

Since it is impossible to process all available environmental stimuli at any given moment, we select and attend to specific information. Combs and Snygg (1959) call the information we focus on *figure* and describe the rest of our experience as *ground*. Our focus, then, is always limited, and this situation explains why two people's perceptions of the same episode are often dissimilar. Through selective attention and/or inattention we tend—because of interest or personal investment—to see those events that would be reinforcing.

An *expectancy effect* is also operative, so that our predictions about the future are based on what we have seen in the past. And what we predict (and expect to see) is largely what we do see.

---

### Individual Activity
### Selective Perception: A Self-Assessment

Recall a recent situation in which you and another person perceived the same episode differently. How did you see the situation? How did the other person see it? How did you communicate about it? Within the context of this particular situation, provide an example of selective attention, selective inattention, and expectancy effect.

**EXAMPLE:**

**Situation:**   I went to a party with Rob at his friend's apartment. Rob knew almost everyone there, and I didn't know anyone.

**Your Perception of the Situation:**   I thought Rob ignored me all night and flirted with every other woman at the party.

**Other's Perception of the Situation:**   He was enjoying seeing old friends again. He said he was being friendly but not flirting. He also did not think he had ignored me.

**How Did You Communicate about the Situation:**   On the ride home I was first silent. Then I got hostile and told him I'd never go with him to another of his friend's parties. I told him his friends were moronic and I didn't enjoy standing around watching him flirt all night.

**Selective Attention:**   I noticed every time Rob talked to, looked at, danced with, smiled at, or joked with another woman. To me it seemed as if this was all he did all night.

**Selective Inattention:**   I didn't notice and/or forgot about the times when Rob came over to talk or dance with me. He said that he spent more time with me than anyone else. As he recounted the time we had been together I remembered it, but at the time I hardly noticed.

**Expectancy Effect:**     When Rob first told me about the party I told him I didn't want to go. I was sure I would have a terrible time since Rob would become the life of the party and I would end up sitting silently in some corner. This is largely what did happen.

**Situation:** _____
_____

**Your Perception of the Situation:** _____
_____

**Other's Perception of the Situation:** _____
_____
_____

**How Did You Communicate about the Situation:** _____
_____
_____
_____

**Selective Attention:** _____
_____
_____

**Selective Inattention:** _____
_____
_____
_____

**Expectancy Effect:** _____
_____
_____
_____

## Interpreting the Behaviors We Have Perceived

We not only pay attention to different environmental cues, but we may interpret the same information in different ways. Actually, our interpretations of what we perceive are more important than the information itself, since our actions are often based on our interpretations.

It is possible to interpret correctly, but there is also enormous room for error. Imagine, for example, that you invite a new acquaintance to your place for dinner. Your invitation is declined on grounds that this person's parents are coming to town for the weekend. How might you interpret this behavior? You could see it as an honest statement of family responsibility. You could also think of it as a put-down from someone who is not interested in getting to know you. The way you choose to communicate with this person in the future will be greatly influenced by the interpretation you make of the behavior in this instance. Your interpretation of what you perceive, then, has an enormous effect on your communication.

## Individual Activity
## Interpreting Behaviors: Written Practice

Consider the following behaviors. Then write two different interpretations for each.

**EXAMPLE:**   Marv is quiet.

   **a.**   Mary is angry.

   **b.**   Mary is tired.

**1.**   Joan is late for our lunch date.

   **a.** _____

_____

   **b.** _____

_____

**2.**   Georgia did not return your phone call.

   **a.** _____

_____

   **b.** _____

_____

**3.** Herb compliments you frequently.

a. _____

_____

b. _____

_____

Now generate three other situations and then write two different interpretations for each.

**1.** _____

a. _____

_____

b. _____

_____

**2.** _____

a. _____

_____

b. _____

_____

**3.** _____

a. _____

_____

b. _____

_____

**Small Group/Class Activity**
**Perceiving and Interpreting Behavior: A Role Reversal Assignment**

Some interpersonal problems can be traced to errors in perception and interpretation. Incorrect assumptions are often left unverified because it is impossible to jump out of your skin and into another's. It is possible to switch positions, however, in a role-play situation. Doing so will help you to better understand the perceptual world of the other person. Try this strategy on a problem area you have been trying to resolve with someone. It may be a recurring argument about curfew, irritating habits, expectations, leisure time, childcare, or household tasks.

Using the form provided, you and the other person involved should try to assess the situation from the *other person's perspective*. What does this person want from the situation? How does this person want the problem to be resolved? How does this person perceive your behavior? How does this person interpret your behavior? When each of you has completed an assessment form, begin to discuss the problem area from *each other's* perspective. Doing so means that you will not be yourself in this situation: You will be role playing the other person.

Since this activity is somewhat complicated, your instructor may want to demonstrate it for you. If so, this can be done easily in a teacher/student role play where a student takes the role of instructor, and the instructor plays that student. The rest of the class can get some practice in filling out the assessment form by dividing into two groups. One group will help the student to fill out the form. The other group will aid the instructor.

## Role Reversal Assessment Form

**EXAMPLE:**

**Problem Area to Be Resolved:**    My husband and I continually argue about which one of us should be responsible for certain household tasks.

**How Does the Other Person Want the Problem to Be Resolved?**    He wants me to do more cleaning and cooking. He wants me to pick up after myself so that my clothes don't mess up our room. He doesn't want to wash dishes but he will help with the house cleaning.

**How Does This Person Perceive Your Behavior?**    He perceives me as being messy and not putting in my share of cleaning and cooking. He sees me doing very little cleaning, dusting, vacuuming, laundry. He agrees that I do dishes more frequently than he does.

**How Does This Person Interpret Your Behavior?**    He thinks I'm taking advantage of him and being irresponsible. He thinks I'm not taking his feelings into consideration and not acknowledging his efforts.

## Role Reversal Assessment Form

**Problem Area to Be Resolved:** _____

_____

_____

**How Does the Other Person Want the Problem to Be Resolved?** _____

_____

_____

**How Does This Person Perceive Your Behavior?** _____

_____

_____

**How Does This Person Interpret Your Behavior?** _____

_____

_____

**Role Reversal Assessment Form**

**Problem Area to Be Resolved:** _____

_____

_____

**How Does the Other Person Want the Problem to Be Resolved?** _____

_____

_____

**How Does This Person Perceive Your Behavior?** _____

_____

_____

**How Does This Person Interpret Your Behavior?** _____

_____

_____

## Perception Checking: Reducing Error by Clarifying Perceptions and Interpretations

Behavior may be received and interpreted correctly, but sometimes we are wrong. The problem is that we have no way of knowing the accuracy of our perceptions and interpretations unless we check them out. Since the purpose of this book is to help you engage in active behavior change, the remainder of this chapter will focus on a procedure for verifying the accuracy of your perceptions.

*Perception checking* is a process that involves describing to your relational partner the specific behaviors you are perceiving and the interpretations you are making about those behaviors. It is critical that these interpretations be phrased tentatively rather than definitely, for perception checking means that you are trying to validate your interpretation. The assumption is that your perceptions may not be accurate. And it is up to your partner to clarify that point.

Imagine, for example, that you are sitting in your apartment waiting for your roommate to arrive. When your roommate returns he or she throws books on the table, walks into the bedroom, and slams the door. You perceive these actions and interpret them to mean something. You may assume that your roommate is angry with you. If you believe this anger is unjustified, you might then become angry in turn. If you neglect to check out your perception and interpretation, an anger cycle could spiral even if it is based on faulty assumptions.

An alternative, then, is to engage in perception checking. You might say to your roommate, "When you came home you threw your books on the table and went into your room, slamming the door without speaking to me. I interpreted that to mean that you were angry about something I had done. Is that true?" Your roommate might agree with your interpretation or might provide an alternative explanation, saying, for example, "I am not angry at you. I just flunked a midterm that I thought I did well on." In this case your perception checking allowed you to verify what had been a faulty interpretation of your roommate's action. Perception checking, then, is one of our alternatives for clarifying and verifying our interpretations of other people's behavior.

---

**Individual Activity or Small Group Rehearsal**
**Perception Checking: Written Practice**

List three possible inferences that you could draw from each of the following behavior descriptions. Then write a perception check using one of those inferences.

**1.** You have noticed that a fellow student in one of your classes is listless. He doesn't smile at you any more and leaves class immediately after it is dismissed. These behaviors are all contrary to this person's usual behavior.

**Inference 1:** _____

_____

**Inference 2:** _____

_____

**Inference 3:** _____

_____

**Perception Check:** _____

_____

_____

**2.** A friend storms into your apartment, ignores you completely, throws books on the table, plops down on the sofa, and opens a magazine that is lying nearby.

**Inference 1:** _____

_____

**Inference 2:** _____

_____

**Inference 3:** _____

_____

**Perception Check:** _____

_____

_____

**3.** A month ago you began to notice that a teenage sister (or friend) was away from home more frequently in the evenings.

**Inference 1:** _____

_____

**Inference 2:** _____

_____

**Inference 3:** _____

_____

**Perception Check:** _____

_____

_____

**4.** A friend of yours doesn't spend much time with you anymore. You used to spend at least one night a week together. Then, about a month ago, you began to notice that whenever you asked him to go somewhere he refused. You also noticed that your friend no longer initiates times together with you.

**Inference 1:** _____

_____

**Inference 2:** _____

_____

**Inference 3:** _____

_____

**Perception Check:** _____

_____

_____

**5.**  Describe a situation from your own experience from which you might draw several inferences. List three inferences and then develop a perception check using one of those inferences.

**Situation:** _____

_____

_____

_____

**Inference 1:** _____

_____

**Inference 2:** _____

_____

**Inference 3:** _____

_____

**Perception Check:** _____

_____

_____

**Individual Activity**
**Perception Checking: Self-Monitoring**

Record three recent incidents in which you didn't check out your perceptions. What might you have said in these situations?

| Behavior of Other | Your Inference | Perception Check You Might Have Made |
|---|---|---|
| 1. _____ | _____ | _____ |
| _____ | _____ | _____ |
| _____ | _____ | _____ |
| _____ | _____ | _____ |
| _____ | _____ | _____ |
| _____ | _____ | _____ |
| _____ | _____ | _____ |
| 2. _____ | _____ | _____ |
| _____ | _____ | _____ |
| _____ | _____ | _____ |
| _____ | _____ | _____ |
| _____ | _____ | _____ |
| _____ | _____ | _____ |
| _____ | _____ | _____ |
| 3. _____ | _____ | _____ |
| _____ | _____ | _____ |
| _____ | _____ | _____ |
| _____ | _____ | _____ |
| _____ | _____ | _____ |
| _____ | _____ | _____ |
| _____ | _____ | _____ |

**Small Group Activity**
**Perception Checking: Behavior Rehearsal**

In groups of five or six prepare and present a role-play situation in which one person's communication is affected by another's differing perceptions and interpretations of the same activating event. Do not use perception checking at this time. Following the presentation of each role play, conduct a class discussion that focuses on how communication problems might have been prevented by perception checking. Based on responses from the class, replay the situation using perception checking.

**Individual Activity**
**Perception Checking: Actual Practice**

During the next weeks check out at least one perception. Describe the situation and the consequences of your perception check in the spaces provided.

**Situation (Behavior of Other):** _____

_____

_____

_____

**Your Interpretation:** _____

_____

_____

_____

**Perception Check You Made:** _____

_____

_____

_____

**Consequences:** _____

_____

_____

_____

_____

**Situation (Behavior of Other):** _____
_____
_____
_____

**Your Interpretation:** _____
_____
_____
_____

**Perception Check You Made:** _____
_____
_____
_____

**Consequences:** _____
_____
_____
_____
_____

# 4 Language

When we speak, we have a particular meaning that we intend to communicate to our listener. The language choices that we make as we encode our message can enhance the probability that our listener will decode our intended idea. You have no doubt had many moments when you expressed your ideas in vivid detail to a friend.

At other times someone misinterpreted your words. The message may have become confused, and you said, "I really didn't mean it that way. " At times, this confusion occurs when we use abstract language. We have less shared meaning for abstract words than we do for concrete ones; for example, to say, "Mary is nice" provides less information than to say, "Mary asks me questions about my family, so I feel she cares about me. "

Although abstract language certainly has a place, letting us generalize and predict interpersonal situations, we can get bogged down in conversations that are vague and ambiguous. No matter how many times we hear that Mary is "nice, " we may continue to wonder what Mary does and says that makes her so likeable. Vivid, specific word choices provide that essential detail in interpersonal talk. By selecting precise descriptions of what we observe, we speakers can add vital information to our messages. When you complete this chapter, you will be more skilled at selecting language that captures the meaning you wish to convey. Your practice with concrete, precise, detailed, and responsible language will increase the probability that the impact of your messages will correspond more closely with your intentions.

## Individual Activity
## Climbing Down the Abstraction Ladder

This activity is designed to give you practice arranging words according to their level of abstraction. In the blanks provided below each word, write three different behavior descriptions, each of which is more concrete (less abstract) than the original word provided. Remember to describe specific behaviors as you complete this exercise. If you discover a large number of adjectives or adverbs, you will need to come down an additional level of abstraction until you are describing actual behavior.

**EXAMPLE:**    Considerate

    **a.**    She asks me if I need anything before she goes shopping.

    **b.**    She keeps the volume of her stereo very low when I'm studying.

    **c.**    When she has a date and I don't, she invites me to come with her.

1.    Helpful

    **a.**    _____

    **b.**    _____

    **c.**    _____

2.    Snobbish

    **a.**    _____

    **b.**    _____

    **c.**    _____

3.    Selfish

    **a.**    _____

    **b.**    _____

    **c.**    _____

4.    Practical

    **a.**    _____

    **b.**    _____

    **c.**    _____

5.    Loving

    **a.**    _____

    **b.**    _____

    **c.**    _____

**6.** Intelligent

    **a.** _____

    **b.** _____

    **c.** _____

**7.** Clumsy

    **a.** _____

    **b.** _____

    **c.** _____

**8.** Mature

    **a.** _____

    **b.** _____

    **c.** _____

### Identifying and Translating Troublesome Language

Chapter 4 of *Interplay* discusses some problems inherent in language: polarization, fact-inference confusion, allness, static evaluation. In addition, some difficulties in the use of words were described: equivocal words, relative words, emotive words, euphemisms, fiction words, abstract words.

   For each of the sentences below first label the language problems you identify. Then rewrite each statement with more precise language.

**EXAMPLE:**

**1.** Politicians are arrogant.

**Language Problems:**   Relative, abstract, emotive wording; indiscriminate terms

**Revised Statement:**   I heard Senator Stark speak to our union and I thought his lecture on the labor movement presumed the rest of us knew nothing about labor history. I call that arrogant.

**2.** She is a bookworm.

**Language Problems:** _____

**Revised Statement:** _____

_____

**3.** Minorities are treated unfairly in the United States.

**Language Problems:** _____

**Revised Statement:** _____

**4.** There are two kinds of people in this world—the givers and the takers.

**Language Problems:** _____

**Revised Statement:** _____

**5.** Helen is a trouble maker.

**Language Problems:** _____

**Revised Statement:** _____

**6.** Jayne is jealous and angry.

**Language Problems:** _____

**Revised Statement:** _____

_____

**7.** Honesty is vital, even if it means inflicting pain.

**Language Problems:** _____

**Revised Statement:** _____

_____

**8.** My daughter is mature.

**Language Problems:** _____

**Revised Statement:** _____

_____

**9.** Teenagers don't care enough about national affairs.

**Language Problems:** _____

**Revised Statement:** _____

_____

For the next few days observe and record examples of some of the troublesome language problems described in Chapter 4 of *Interplay*. Pay particular attention to those situations in which this kind of language usage had a negative impact on some communication event. How might these messages have been more clearly and effectively communicated?

**Language of
Responsibility**

In Chapter 10 you will learn that interpersonal climate can be enhanced when people "own" their messages—when they take responsibility for what they do and believe. "You" messages put the responsibility on the receiver rather than the sender where it belongs. In addition to "you" language, "it, " "we, " and "question" messages all have the capacity to divest the speaker of responsibility. Although these messages are often less threatening because they reveal less of our own thoughts and feelings, they also do little to promote relational growth. We remain virtual strangers to each other as long as we fail to communicate about what makes us personally unique.

Consider the following statements:

"It will be nice to see each other again."
"It was great having you here."

Although the speaker in both cases probably believed that personal feelings were being revealed, little is actually being disclosed. If the statement were translated into self-responsible "I" language, we would learn more about the speaker's feelings:

"I feel so appreciated and secure when you're here. I hope you come back soon."

Similar language problems occur with "we" language or questions. By not specifically describing the sender's thoughts and feelings, "we" and "question" statements also avoid responsibility.

---

**Individual Activity**
**Language of Responsibility: Written Practice**

For each of the following statements, first identify the problem and then rewrite the statement using responsible "I" language.

**EXAMPLE:**   *"It bothers me* when you're late."

**Problem:**   "It" evades responsibility for feelings.

**Responsible Alternative:**   "I worry when you're late."

**1.**  "We should go out more often."

**Problem:** _____

**Responsible Alternative:** _____

_____

**2.**  "You're so selfish. Why did you do that?"

**Problem:** _____

**Responsible Alternative:** _____

_____

**3.**  "It's not fair. How would you like it if I treated you that way?"

**Problem:** _____

**Responsible Alternative:** _____

_____

**4.**  "We should start dating other people."

**Problem:** _____

**Responsible Alternative:** _____

_____

**5.** "It's hard to talk about your feelings."

**Problem:** _____

**Responsible Alternative:** _____

_____

**6.** "We haven't been alone for a long time."

**Problem:** _____

**Responsible Alternative:** _____

_____

**7.** "Don't you think that learning new things is exciting?"

**Problem:** _____

**Responsible Alternative:** _____

_____

**8.** "Isn't it hard to speak to strangers?"

**Problem:** _____

**Responsible Alternative:** _____

_____

**9.** "It's easy to talk to you."

**Problem:** _____

**Responsible Alternative:** _____

_____

**10.** "It's really great to have a good friend like you to count on."

**Problem:** _____

**Responsible Alternative:** _____

_____

_____

_____

## Language of Detail: Pinpointing and Documenting

The direct and unambiguous expression of feelings is an important interpersonal skill. Yet if you neglect to provide your listener with pinpointed behavior descriptions, the meaning of your messages may be confusing. Consider the following statement:

> "I feel scared and sad because I am not as close to you as I used to be."

This message is communicated in responsible "I" language; the speaker has "owned" and directly expressed feelings. Yet something critical is missing: a description of the behavioral referents on which the feelings about lack of closeness are based. What actual behaviors has this person observed? On what sense data have the feelings, inferences, evaluations, been based?

Without pinpointing and documenting the person receiving this message is put in an untenable position where a considerable amount of guessing and inferring becomes necessary. The need for speculation is reduced when behavioral referents are provided. Our example could be modified in the following way:

> "I feel scared and sad because I'm not as close to you as I used to be. We used to tell each other about our fears and concerns, but for the past six months, our conversations have been almost entirely about school work."

When our language is more specific and descriptive, receivers of our messages are given more information with which to respond.

---

### Individual Activity
### Language of Detail: Written Practice

Rewrite each of the following statements using *responsible* "I" language as well as pinpointing and documenting. Each revised statement should contain a direct and unambiguous expression of feelings as well as a description of the behavioral referent on which the feeling is based.

**EXAMPLE:**  "You've really been putting me down lately."

**Revised Statement:**  Yesterday when you told Jon that I was an incompetent driver I felt put down and unappreciated."

**Statement 1:**  "You're the best teacher I've ever had."

**Revised Statement:** _____

_____

_____

_____

_____

_____

**Statement 2:** "You've become so insensitive to my needs."

**Revised Statement:** _____

_____

_____

_____


**Statement 3:** "I really messed things up with my sister yesterday."

**Revised Statement:** _____

_____

_____

_____


**Statement 4:** "A lot of things are really bothering me."

**Revised Statement:** _____

_____

_____

_____


**Statement 5:** "How can you be so rude and thoughtless?"

**Revised Statement:** _____

_____

_____

_____


**Statement 6:** "You don't care about what happens to me."

**Revised Statement:** _____

_____

_____

_____

_____

_____

_____

## Language of Intention

Often when we describe our feelings to someone it is because we want to see something happen. We want the other person to do something to help us feel better, to change a behavior that is personally bothersome, or to help us work out a problem. Yet seldom do we make these intentions clear and unambiguous. On the contrary, we often hint in vague terms and then expect others to read our minds and figure out what we want. "If he really cared about me, he'd know what I want," is an often heard refrain among distressed couples. So is "If I have to tell her then it becomes meaningless."

Although we have probably all had thoughts similar to these, it is hazardous to expect another person to have this implicit understanding of our intentions. Since many people are unaware of their own intentions, to expect other people to be aware of what we want is, at best, unrealistic. Therefore, we want to describe our intentions in direct, unambiguous language, so that our interpersonal partners have a clearer understanding of what we want them to do. Simply put, a *description of intention* is a statement of what you would like the other person to do differently, how you would like that person to behave towards you.

Consider the following statement: "I feel angry. You are thirty minutes late for our appointment." In this statement the speaker has directly expressed feelings of anger and described the behavioral referent on which the feeling is based. Yet the receiver of the message is given no specific direction for behavior change and has little choice but to accept the statement as nothing more than punishment. By adding an intention description to the statement, you tell the speaker what you would like to see done differently the next time. For example, you might add, "It would help me if you would call when you can't make it on time." Statements that contain feeling descriptions, pinpointing, and intention descriptions, do reduce ambiguity and increase clarity.

---

### Individual Activity
### Language of Intention: Written Practice

Return to the "Language of Detail: Written Practice" activity (p. 63). For each of your pinpointed feeling descriptions now include an intention description as part of the statement. This addition means that each statement should now contain a feeling description, behavior documentation, and intention description.

**EXAMPLE:**    "You've really been putting me down lately."

**Revised Statement:**    Yesterday when you told Jon that I was an incompetent driver, I felt put down and unappreciated. I'd prefer that you not make negative comments about my driving to other people.

**Statement 1:**   "You're the best teacher I've ever had."

**Revised Statement:** _____

_____

_____

_____

**Statement 2:**   "You've become so insensitive to my needs."

**Revised Statement:** _____

_____

_____

_____

**Statement 3:**   "I really messed things up with my sister yesterday."

**Revised Statement:** _____

_____

_____

_____

**Statement 4:**   "A lot of things are really bothering me."

**Revised Statement:** _____

_____

_____

_____

**Statement 5:**   "How can you be so rude and thoughtless?"

**Revised Statement:** _____

_____

_____

_____

**Statement 6:**   "You don't care about what happens to me."

**Revised Statement:** _____

_____

_____

_____

_____

**Individual Activity**
**Communicating Pleasure and Displeasure: A Review**

The next activity gives you an opportunity to bring together four important language skills: responsible "I" statements, feeling descriptions, intention descriptions, and pinpointing and documenting. Since you need to practice these behaviors communicating both positive and negative messages, begin by thinking of three things that people do that please you, and three things that displease you. You may be thinking about six different people or one person on six different occasions.

Then, on the form provided, develop three statements that communicate pleasure and three that communicate displeasure. Each statement should contain all four of the language skills discussed. Identify each of these components in your statements.

**EXAMPLE:**

**Statement of Pleasure:**   "Yesterday when you came home early from work to be with me [pinpointing], I felt ["I" statement] appreciated and loved [feeling description]. I want you to know that seeing you meant a lot to me [intention description]."

**EXAMPLE:**

**Statement of Displeasure:**   "When you cancelled our dinner plans without checking with me first [pinpointing], I felt ["I" statement] ignored [feeling description]. I'd like you to ask me what my preference is before you include me in your plans [intention description]."

**Statement of Pleasure 1:** _____

_____

_____

_____

_____

**Statement of Pleasure 2:** _____

_____

_____

_____

_____

**Statement of Pleasure 3:** _____

_____

_____

_____

_____

_____

**Statement of Displeasure 1:** _____

_____

_____

_____

_____

**Statement of Displeasure 2:** _____

_____

_____

_____

_____

**Statement of Displeasure 3:** _____

_____

_____

_____

_____

### Facilitative Language: Implementation In Real Situations

Now you will have an opportunity to actually use the language behaviors you have been learning in real situations. What follows is a five-step procedure to help you generalize what you have learned about facilitative language and apply that knowledge to your everyday life.

**1.   Choosing a Topic:**   Choose an issue or problem you wish to discuss with some person. Since this may be the first time you are implementing these language behaviors in a real situation, be sure to choose an issue, problem, or behavior with which you have a reasonable chance of succeeding. The issue should be something about which you have feelings and a specific intention. Choose a situation that you are not completely satisfied with at the present time, one that involves another person's behavior to some extent. In the spaces that follow describe the issue or problem you have chosen:

_____

_____

_____

_____

_____

_____

_____

**2.    Covert Rehearsal:**    Now, in a quiet space, close your eyes and actually think about yourself communicating your message to the person involved. Be certain that your message is phrased in nonaccusatory language and accepts responsibility with ''I'' statements, feeling description, intention description, and pinpointing. Imagine yourself communicating this message in at least three or four different ways, varying specific word choice and number and length of sentences. Next, in the space provided, record the language that you are most pleased with. Then label each of the language skills in your message.

_____

_____

_____

_____

_____

_____

_____

_____

**3.    Behavior Rehearsal:**    Now rehearse your message in groups of five or six people. Describe to another group member the role of the person who would be receiving your message in the actual situation. Suggest any possible negative reactions you may receive from this person. If your behavior rehearsal seems to go too easily, have your role play partner make it more difficult by refusing your request as unreasonable, denying the right for you to feel the way you do, claiming you are overreacting. Now get feedback from the other group members concerning what they liked most about your behavior in this situation, and also any suggestions they might have. Then, based on the suggestions from your group, rehearse the situation one more time. If you are having trouble with a particularly difficult situation, you may want to go through this process again.

**4.    Implementation of Actual Behavior:**    Plan on a specific time to actually communicate your message to the person involved. Decide on a time that seems reasonable and appropriate and tell your group when you plan to do it.

**5.    Evaluation:**    After you have communicated your message to the person actually involved, it is useful to evaluate your behavior, which does _not_ mean you will evaluate yourself according to whether or not the receiver of your message complied with your intention. Rather, you will evaluate _your own_ communication.

**What did you like about what you did?**

_____

_____

_____

_____

_____

## What would you prefer to do differently?

_____

_____

_____

_____

_____

Now report this information to your group, and get input from the other group members.

# 5 Nonverbal Communication

In the last 25 years, communication experts have come to appreciate the tremendous impact nonverbal behavior has upon interpersonal interactions. We now know that people communicate emotions and feelings primarily in the nonverbal mode. When we describe the communication process completely, we must include both verbal and nonverbal elements. In actual interactions, verbal and nonverbal communication usually occur simultaneously.

For the purpose of learning to observe and practice nonverbal skills, Chapter 5 separates the nonverbal elements from spoken words. Each dimension of nonverbal behavior is discussed initially as a separate element. As you are learning to analyze communication, you will find it useful to examine particular dimensions of nonverbal behavior. Later in the chapter you will discover how nonverbal dimensions combine and synchronize with verbal messages to produce a total impression.

When you complete this chapter you should be more aware of your own nonverbal communication and what it may suggest to others. Because of this heightened awareness you should become more skilled at developing congruency between your verbal and nonverbal messages. You should also be able to communicate nonverbally in a manner that is consistent with your situational goals.

**Individual Activity**
**Paralanguage: Our Voice Communicates**

*Paralanguage* refers to how something is said. A given bit of information can be communicated in countless ways, and the impact or meaning of a message is strongly influenced by the paralanguage that accompanies it. Paralanguage refers to pitch, volume, rate, nonfluencies ("um," "uh," etc.), and pauses. These are the qualifiers that accompany verbal messages and tell us how to interpret them.

To gain a clearer understanding of the effects of paralanguage, repeat each of the following two messages four times, varying pitch, volume, rate, nonfluencies and pauses to suggest nervousness, sarcasm, anger, and boredom.

**Message 1:**   "I'd like to get to know you better."

**Message 2:**   "I really enjoyed this evening. I don't know when I've had more fun."

Which elements of paralanguage seemed particularly relevant to changing the implied meanings of the messages? Were certain elements of paralanguage more applicable to specific emotions?

**Individual Activity**
**Paralanguage: Self-Monitoring**

What happens to your voice when you are in a high stress situation? When you are angry? Sad? Happy? Excited? Bored? Monitor your own paralanguage for the next few days and attempt to assess how it varies according to your emotional state. Record your self-monitoring data on the following chart.

| Emotion | Pauses | Pitch (High/Low) | Volume (Loud/Soft) | Rate (Fast/Slow) | Nonfluencies | Tone (Harsh/Soft) |
|---------|--------|------------------|--------------------|------------------|--------------|-------------------|
| Angry   |        |                  |                    |                  |              |                   |
| Sad     |        |                  |                    |                  |              |                   |
| Happy   |        |                  |                    |                  |              |                   |
| Excited |        |                  |                    |                  |              |                   |
| Bored   |        |                  |                    |                  |              |                   |

**Individual Activity**
**Kinesics: Our Body Communicates**

Paralanguage is only one form of nonverbal communication. We also communicate nonverbally through facial expressions, gestures, body position, and movement. We often interpret a great deal about a person's emotional state by observing *kinesic patterns*. For the next few days observe and record the emotional states you associate with certain facial expressions, eye behavior, gestures, body position, and movement. Use the form provided to record your data.

## Kinesic Behaviors

| | Facial Expressions | Gestures | Body Position | Movement |
|---|---|---|---|---|
| Tense | | | | |
| Relaxed | | | | |
| Angry | | | | |
| Happy | | | | |
| Sad | | | | |
| Bored | | | | |

**Emotional States Observed**

## Eye Contact: Regulating Conversation

We have all experienced some of the powerful effects of interpersonal gazing. From infancy on, we watch the eyes of people in interaction for many cues as to feelings and appropriate behavior. We say we are "making eyes" of romantic interest or "looking daggers" of anger.

Both emotional content and the regulation of conversational flow are conveyed in part by eye contact. Observe your classmates or small group members for the next few meetings to discover how these patterns operate.

## Individual Activity
## Eye Contact

| Eye Behavior | Communication Outcome |
|---|---|
| 1. **EXAMPLE:** | |
| Mutual eye contact— "catching your eye." | We begin to talk. |
| 2. **EXAMPLE:** | |
| Looking at partner as you end your statement. | The partner takes a conversation turn. |

## Small Group Activity
## Nonverbal Communication: Environmental Elements

You have probably had the experience of visiting a friend's home where you immediately felt comfortable and relaxed. Physical environments affect the nature, quality, and amount of communication among people.

As a group, develop a statement about the relationship between physical environment and communication. Consider these issues:

1. Where do you live? How does the structure of space affect to whom you talk? Which neighbors do you know best?

2. If you share your living space with someone, have you established territory as your own? How?

3. In your classrooms how does the layout affect teacher–student and student–student interaction? How does the layout affect participation?

4. When you've felt comfortable at a friend's home, what things about the rooms promoted your communication? When you've been uncomfortable, what environmental factors contributed?

5. How do you prepare your environment for a party? For a romantic encounter?

## Individual Activity
## Personal Territory: A Field Study

For the next week observe and report on some typical procedures used by people to establish *personal territory* in public places. How do people establish their own territory in a new classroom? How do people define the limits of their territory in public places such as libraries, dining halls, and cafeterias? What kinds of "personal markers" do people use in these situations? Describe a situation where you thought your territory had been invaded. How did you feel? What did you do?

## Individual Activity
## Touch: Self-Monitoring

In Chapter 5 of *Interplay*, you read about touching as a form of nonverbal communication. Touch can express many positive messages: attention (a tap on the shoulder), encouragement (a pat on the back), support (an arm around the shoulder). Yet touch has many restrictions in Western culture, and violations of touch taboos may bring a close to interactions. In order to explore how touch affects you and those around you, keep track of your touching and being touched behaviors for a week.

| Touch Situation | Touching Behavior | Response |
|---|---|---|
| **EXAMPLE:**<br>Meeting my roommate's friend. | I offered my hand. | He shook hands and smiled. |

**Individual Activity**
**Physical Appearance**

Especially in early phases of social contact, our personal appearance can be crucial. People make judgments before we even begin to speak. Planning the impact of your appearance can be an important interpersonal skill. Take a few minutes to describe the ways you focus your nonverbal appearance in the following interpersonal settings.

| Occasion | Clothing and Decoration | Hair | Face |
|---|---|---|---|
| **EXAMPLE:** Job interview | My gray wool suit and white silk blouse. Black shoes, pearl earrings. | Pull up. | Light make-up. |
| Party in dorm | | | |
| Exercise with my friend | | | |
| Dinner with friend's parents | | | |
| Costume party | | | |

## Small Group Activity
## Nonverbal Behavior and Interpersonal Competence

The first part of this chapter was designed to increase your awareness of nonverbal behavior and its impact on verbal messages. Now let's focus on some competencies and skills associated with nonverbal communication.

Interpersonal competence is difficult to define, but it is clear that kinesics and paralanguage account for part of our ratings of interpersonal skill. The following activity provides you with an opportunity to explore the nonverbal dimensions of interpersonal competence.

Monitor the nonverbal behavior of someone you perceive to be a competent, confident, assertive communicator. Do the same for someone you perceive to be nervous, apprehensive, or anxious about communicating. What differences do you see in their nonverbal behaviors?

| Name of Confident Communicator: _____ | Name of Anxious Communicator: _____ |
| --- | --- |
| **Competent, Confident, Assertive Nonverbal Behaviors:** (Include voice, facial expressions, gestures, body position, movement.) | **Nervous, Apprehensive, Anxious Nonverbal Behaviors:** (Include voice, facial expressions, gestures, body position, movement.) |
| **EXAMPLE:** Smiling; leaning in toward the other person. | **EXAMPLE:** Biting fingernails; eyes gazing at floor. |

Now, in small groups, design a role play that demonstrates and illustrates the nonverbal behaviors you identified in the assignment. Present the groups' role plays to the rest of the class. Did the groups identify similar or different nonverbal indicators of competence and apprehension? Following these role plays, class discussion should focus on the relationship between nonverbal behavior and communication competence. What do these findings suggest about teaching apprehensive communicators to be more skilled?

## Nonverbal Communication: Congruity/ Incongruity

Nonverbal communication often helps us to interpret verbal messages. When verbal and nonverbal expressions carry the same meaning and belong together, we say they are *congruent*. Let us suppose, for example, that your date says, "I'm having a really good time," while smiling, maintaining eye contact, moving closer to you, and touching your hand. In this situation the verbal message is congruent with the nonverbal.

What would happen, however, if this same verbal message were communicated with different nonverbal behaviors? Suppose, for example, that this time your date is staring off into space, looking at a wristwatch, moving back in the chair and frowning? In this situation the verbal and nonverbal messages would be *incongruent* and you would have a difficult time interpreting the meaning of the message.

**Individual Activity**
**Incongruity: Monitoring Its Occurrence**

Monitor and record at least two different situations in which you observed verbal and nonverbal messages that were incongruent. What problems did this create? How were the messages interpreted? What might have been done to correct the situation? Use the form provided to record your observations.

| Situation | Verbal Behavior | Nonverbal Behavior (voice, facial expressions, gestures, body position, movement) | Response to Incongruity |
|---|---|---|---|
| **EXAMPLE:** Child spills milk, then says to mother, "Don't be mad." | Mother replies, "I'm not mad." | **Voice:**   Loud volume, slow, steady rate; no variation in pitch.<br><br>**Facial Expressions:**   No eye contact; eyes squinted, glaring.<br><br>**Body Position:**   Posture stiff.<br><br>**Gestures:**   Pointing index finger at child.<br><br>**Movement:**   Grabs child's napkin and wipes up milk. | Child seems to observe the incongruity and says, "I know you're mad. Why are you mad?" |

## Nonverbal Attention:
## Listening with Action

People speaking to you are completely unaware of your covert behavior—your thoughts, feelings, interpretations; beliefs are private events observable only to you. Although you may be listening with a high degree of intensity and interest, if your nonverbal behavior does not communicate this attention, the person speaking to you will probably believe you are bored, disinterested, or even hostile. The following activities will give you an opportunity to discover the nonverbal behaviors that communicate attention and inattention.

## Dyad Activity
## An Exercise in Nonverbal Attention

This activity is to be done in dyads. After your class has paired off and each person has a partner, decide who will speak first and who will listen. As the speaker, your task is to relate an especially significant or exciting idea, feeling, or experience. Try as hard as you can to get your listener involved in what you are saying. As the listener, your task is to give no signs of nonverbal attention: no "umhums," no smiles, nods, facial expressions—nothing. After the speaker has talked for three minutes, switch roles.

When you have completed both rounds of this assignment, discuss what it felt like to: (a) receive no nonverbal attention; and (b) give no nonverbal attention. Which was more difficult to do? Why?

Now replay this activity sending the same messages, but this time attending nonverbally. Still, as the listener, you should not make any verbal input, but your *nonverbal* input should be significant. When you have completed this assignment consider the following questions: As the speaker, what was the most significant difference you found in relating your message to a nonverbally attentive listener? How did you feel? Did it affect your message in any way? As a listener, how were you affected by attending nonverbally? Did it have any impact on your covert listening? Did you feel any different? What do you think is the effect of nonverbal attention on interpersonal episodes?

**Small Group Activity**
**Attention and Inattention: Nonverbal Dimensions**

In groups of five to seven use the form provided to brainstorm a list of nonverbal behaviors that indicate whether or not a person is listening. The intent here is for you to describe what listeners do nonverbally to communicate attention and inattention.

| Nonverbal Inattention | Nonverbal Attention |
|---|---|
| **EXAMPLE:** No eye contact; staring at the floor or off into space. | **EXAMPLE:** Looking at person speaking; maintaining eye contact. |
| 1. _____ | 1. _____ |
| 2. _____ | 2. _____ |
| 3. _____ | 3. _____ |
| 4. _____ | 4. _____ |
| 5. _____ | 5. _____ |
| 6. _____ | 6. _____ |
| 7. _____ | 7. _____ |
| 8. _____ | 8. _____ |
| 9. _____ | 9. _____ |
| 10. _____ | 10. _____ |

### Observing and Interpreting Nonverbal Behavior: A Three-Part Assignment

Since nonverbal behavior is ambiguous, it is important to treat your interpretations of others' actions as hunches that must be verified. The next assignment will help you to understand more clearly some of the problems associated with interpreting another person's nonverbal behavior.

Begin by choosing a regularly seen partner who will be willing to talk with you about your interpretations of his or her nonverbal behavior. For the first two days simply observe and record the ways your partner behaves nonverbally. List your partner's behaviors on the form provided. During this phase of the assignment be sure *not to interpret* your partner's actions. Merely record what you observe. At the end of this two-day period describe your observations to your partner.

### Record of Partner's Nonverbal Behavior

| Situation | Nonverbal Behavior (voice, facial expressions, gestures, body position, movement) |
|---|---|
| **EXAMPLE:**   She came home from work and went to the refrigerator for a beer. There was no beer left. | She slammed the refrigerator door; her lips were tight. She made a "tsk" sound. |

Now, for the next two days not only observe your partner's nonverbal behavior but also *interpret* it. What evaluations did you make from the nonverbal behavior that you observed? What conclusions did you draw? Record this information on the form provided. Then describe your inferences to your partner. This process will allow you to verify the accuracy of your interpretations. How accurate were you?

## Interpretation of Partner's Nonverbal Behavior

| Situation | Nonverbal Behavior (voice, facial expressions, gestures, body position, movement) | Interpretation of Nonverbal Behavior |
|---|---|---|
| **EXAMPLE:** She woke up, opened her drapes, and looked outside. It was raining. | Pulled drapes closed; fell back on to bed; pulled cover over her head. | I thought she was disappointed and annoyed about the weather. Her weekend plans were probably ruined. |

Next, for two additional days monitor your partner's nonverbal behavior, your *interpretations* of that behavior and your resulting *feelings*. Record this information on the form provided. Then discuss these data with your partner. How accurate were your interpretations? How did your partner respond to your feelings about his or her behavior? Were there any situations in which your interpretation (and consequently your feelings) were an inaccurate assessment of your partner's nonverbal behavior?

## Feelings About Partner's Nonverbal Behavior

| Situation | Nonverbal Behavior (voice, facial expressions, gestures, body position, movement) | Interpretation of Nonverbal Behavior | Feelings |
|---|---|---|---|
| **EXAMPLE:** Eating dinner with my husband. | He made no eye contact; facial muscles tight; no smiling; cleared his throat frequently. | He is angry about something I've done. | Sorry for myself; isolated; misunderstood. |

**Individual Activity/Small Group Activity**
**Nonverbal Communication: A Self-Improvement Project**

Now that you have had an opportunity to think about, observe, and interpret nonverbal behavior, consider your own communication and choose a situation in which you want to improve your own nonverbal behavior. You will begin by monitoring your nonverbal behavior in a situation you find particularly difficult. Based on your monitoring, you will then establish a nonverbal goal. Then, you will have an opportunity to rehearse your target behavior. Finally, you will perform and assess your nonverbal behavior in the actual situation.

**1. Monitoring** Monitor your own nonverbal communication in a situation you find particularly difficult: talking to a professor, making a speech, saying "no" to a friend, returning merchandise, talking to your parents, or socializing at a party. On the form provided, describe your nonverbal behavior in the situation you have chosen to work on.

**General situation I have chosen to work on:** _____

_____

| Specific Instance of Situation | My Nonverbal Behavior (voice, facial expressions, gestures, body position, movement) |
|---|---|
| **EXAMPLE:** I went to my English professor's office to ask about the grade I received on my term paper. | I hardly looked at the professor. Instead, I gazed at the floor or around the room. I didn't sit still, but rather kept shifting my body in the chair. I was fidgeting with my fingers and pencil and playing with my hair. My voice was very soft and I spoke in a monotone. I never smiled. |

**2.   Goal Setting**   Now that you have monitored and recorded your own nonverbal behavior in a particular kind of communication situation, review your data and establish a specific goal for change. Write your goal in the space provided. Be certain that it is written in observable, behavioral terms.

**EXAMPLE:**   When I go to speak to a professor, I want to lean back in my chair and rest my hands comfortably on the chair arms. I want to look my professor in the eyes, nod occasionally, smile. I don't want to fidget with my pencil or play with my hair or nails. I want to speak in a strong voice and vary my pitch.

**3.   Rehearsal**   Now form groups of about 5 people. In these groups you will practice your target nonverbal goal. To do this, choose and describe a situation in which your new nonverbal behavior could be used. Have a person in your group play the role of an individual you might be speaking to in the situation you have described. Remember that in this particular assignment the content of your message is less important than the nonverbal elements.

When you have completed this behavior rehearsal, your group should give you specific input about the nonverbal behaviors they observed and any specific recommendations for change they might have. Then rehearse the situation once again, incorporating the group's feedback. Group members should use the form provided to record their observations; make additional copies of the form if needed.

## Group Member Observation Form

**Instructions:**    During each person's behavior rehearsal, record your observations of his or her nonverbal behavior in each of the categories described below.

**Group Member Observed:** _____

**Situation:** _____

_____

**Nonverbal Behaviors:**

1.  **Vocal Characteristics:** _____

_____

_____

_____

2.  **Gestures:** _____

_____

_____

_____

3.  **Body Position:** _____

_____

_____

_____

4.  **Facial Expressions:** _____

_____

_____

_____

5.  **Movement:** _____

_____

_____

_____

**4. Actual Practice**   Now that you have had an opportunity to rehearse your nonverbal behavior in a role play situation, you are ready to practice implementing these new behaviors in the real life situations you chose to work on in the monitoring section. Report the results of this implementation below.

### Record of Real Life Practice

| Situation | Nonverbal Behaviors (vocal characteristics, gestures, body position, facial expressions, movement) | Your Evaluation (what you liked; what you would change) |
|---|---|---|
| **EXAMPLE:** I went to see my History professor about an independent project I wanted to do. | I spoke in a loud, clear voice; my body looked relaxed; I was leaning back slightly in my chair; my hands were resting on the chair arms; I maintained eye contact. I still fidgeted with my rings and pen. | I liked the relaxed appearance of my body. I also liked the loud, clear sound of my voice. I would change the way I fidgeted with my rings and pen. |

## Record of Real Life Practice

| Situation | Nonverbal Behaviors (vocal character-istics, gestures, body position, facial expressions, movement) | Your Evaluation (what you liked; what you would change) |
|-----------|------------------------------------------------------------------------------------------------------|---------------------------------------------------------|
|           |                                                                                                      |                                                         |

# 6 Listening

Our friends often come to us for attention and recognition; they want to tell us about an accomplishment or a defeat. We willingly give important people in our interpersonal systems the gift of our attention. Perhaps the most significant way we show our interest in friends is through our listening skills. In order to respond attentively, we try to hear their message and to relate our responses to what they are saying.

Sometimes we listen passively; although we understand the information, we do not show our understanding. We engage in a cognitive process, but we show no outward sign that we have paid attention to our friend's words and actions. For example, we might listen to a set of directions to a party without commenting, and our friend would reasonably wonder whether we had heard the instructions.

Nonattending listening behavior often communicates disinterest, boredom, disagreement, even hostility. The irony of passive listening is that many times we do not intend to communicate these impressions. Often when we listen to people we really *are* interested in what they have to say; we respect them as people and we are receptive to their ideas. Yet when we are silent and unresponsive listeners, our nonattending behaviors communicate to others intentions that may be quite different from our real ones.

Take a few minutes now to think about all the poor listening behaviors you have observed. If you are having a difficult time with this assignment, observe people listening for only one day and your list will surely lengthen. Describe these behaviors on the form provided.

**Individual Activity**
**Ineffective Listening: An Appraisal**

Think about the poor listening you have observed and record these behaviors on the following chart.

| Person | Circumstances | Listening Behavior |
|---|---|---|
| EXAMPLE: My wife. | We're eating breakfast. I'm telling her about a problem at work. She's reading the paper. | No eye contact. She says an occasional "umhum" but it doesn't always fit with what I'm saying at the time. |
| 1. | | |
| 2. | | |
| 3. | | |
| 4. | | |
| 5. | | |
| 6. | | |
| 7. | | |

**Individual Activity**
**Listening Behavior: A Self-Assessment**

Review the sections in *Interplay,* Chapter 6, on why we do not listen and why we have poor listening habits. Then, for the next two days, observe your own listening behavior to discover instances and reasons for ineffective listening. Use the following form below to record your observations.

| Time | Place | People | Subjects | Listening Behavior | Consequences |
|------|-------|--------|----------|--------------------|--------------| 
| **EXAMPLE:** 8:00 A.M. | Home watching *Monday Night Football* on TV. | My son; myself. | School; his birthday party. I'm not sure what else he talked about because I was usually not listening. | I didn't look at him much. I tried to make him think I was listening by saying "yes," "sure," "umhum." I only really listened to him when he started whining or misbehaving. | He started to have a tantrum and throw his toys; he also kept trying to turn off the TV. |

| Time | Place | People | Subjects | Listening Behavior | Consequences |
|------|-------|--------|----------|--------------------|--------------|
|      |       |        |          |                    |              |

Now review your data. Did you notice any patterns of poor listening behavior? Are there certain times, situations, subjects, or physiological states when your listening is most ineffective? Was your listening ever affected by excessive input, personal concerns, hearing problems, rapid thought, noise? Did you discover any instances of pseudolistening, selective listening, defensive listening or other poor listening habits discussed in *Interplay*? Describe the patterns you discovered on the chart provided.

### Patterns of Poor Listening

1. _____

_____

2. _____

_____

3. _____

_____

4. _____

_____

5. _____

_____

6. _____

_____

7. _____

_____

8. _____

_____

9. _____

_____

10. _____

_____

## Ineffective Listening: Some Common Problems
### Triad Activity

**Part 1: Amount of Input**   There are times when listening is impaired because the amount of input is too extensive for the brain to process. For example, one person may be bombarding you with a great deal of information, or two people may be simultaneously vying for your attention as a listener.

The following activity is designed to put you in a situation where listening is impaired by the amount of input. This activity is to be done in groups of three. While one person is listening, the other two people will, simultaneously, tell that person different stories. This situation is such that, in the role of listener, each person will be hearing two different stories at the same time. Each round should last about four minutes. At the end of this time the listener will attempt to repeat each of the messages received.

How successful were you in hearing both messages? What problems did you have? Were any significant aspects omitted? Does this situation resemble any other kinds of communicative situations in which you find yourself?

### Dyad Activity

**Part 2: Personal Concerns**   The act of listening is also influenced by our personal concerns. Most of us have had the experience of thinking about personally significant problems while listening to another person. When this circumstance occurs we may find ourselves totally unaware of the content of the message we have heard.

The following activity, to be done in dyads, is designed to illustrate the effect of personal concerns on listening. Each person should think of something to tell the other: a story, an event, an experience, or a feeling that is personally significant, meaningful, or interesting. Take turns being the speaker and the listener. When you are in the listening role, think of a personal problem that is significant to you and allow it to interfere with the other person's message. In other words, while the other person is speaking, attempt to think about your problem instead of the speaker's message.

At the end of four or five minutes attempt to describe what you heard to the speaker. How close was your received message to the intended message of the speaker? Were there any significant gaps? How did it feel to be thinking about personal problems while the other person was speaking? As a speaker were you able to detect that the other person was not attentively listening?

## Active Listening: An Approach to Changing Listening Behavior

By now you have grown increasingly aware of the difficulties involved in listening effectively. Hopefully you have also developed an awareness of the vital function of listening in any communication event. The remainder of this chapter will provide you with some specific listening skills or behaviors that will allow you to be a more effective and functional listener.

The term "listening behaviors" may at first sound inappropriate since many people view listening as the passive component of a communicative exchange. If you think of listening as a basically covert, internal activity it may be difficult for you to think about observable, describable listening behaviors. The framework provided in this chapter postulates that listening is as active and behavioral as speaking.

Active responses indicate effective listening.   Listening without responding is of little value to the speaker. As *Interplay* points out: listening is not merely hearing. Thus, let's now concentrate on  some listening behaviors that will allow you to be a more effective, functional, and helpful listener.

Often during conversations people assume they understand each other without bothering to check their assumptions out. Paraphrasing and perception checking are skills that allow you to verify your inferences. When you paraphrase and check out perceptions, you not only clarify the meaning of speakers' messages, but you also let people know that what they say and feel is important to you.

**Paraphrasing: Listening as Verbal Behavior**

Simply defined, *paraphrasing* is a restatement of both the content and feelings of another person's message. When you paraphrase you give the other person information about the impact of his or her message. You may find it easier to paraphrase when you draw a mental picture of what the other person is saying. This technique allows you to become more involved in the transaction and more able to identify and describe the speaker's feelings and experiences.

An enormous amount of misunderstanding and misinterpretation would be eliminated if we used paraphrasing more frequently. It is important to emphasize that paraphrasing is not merely parroting or repeating the speaker's words. The speaker's feelings, sometimes stated indirectly, are often central to the message being communicated and should consequently be included in a paraphrase. When you first begin to paraphrase, you will probably feel a bit awkward. Your new behavior may feel unnatural, uncomfortable, clumsy. But think back to other skills and how you felt when you first learned them. Do you remember what it felt like the first time you drove a stick shift or rode a bike or tried to serve a tennis ball? We expect all new skills to feel uncomfortable or unnatural in the initial learning stages and so we stick with them, practicing to increase comfort and skill. This principle also applies to paraphrasing behavior. Some people have found the following phrases to be useful when they first learn to paraphrase:

"What I think you mean is . . ."
"I hear you saying . . ."
"I understand you to mean . . ."
"Let me see if I can tell you what you're saying . . ."
"It sounds like. . ."
"You feel _____ because _____ . . ."
      (feelings)                    (event, experiences)

Here are some examples of paraphrasing:

**Speaker:**    "I wish I could have finished my term paper by Friday, so I could go skiing, but now I won't be able to go."

**Paraphrase:**    "You sound really disappointed. You were so excited about this ski trip."

**Speaker:**    "I'm just not sure what to do about finishing school. I'm really getting sick of it. But I've come so far and I'm so close to graduating. I don't know whether to stay or to quit."

**Paraphrase:**    "It sounds like you're really torn. On the one hand you're feeling frustrated about school, and yet you're so close to finishing that you're reluctant to quit. This decision is hard for you to make."

---

**Small Group Activity**
**When Paraphrasing Is Inappropriate**

Paraphrasing is not always useful or desirable. Can you think of any situations in which paraphrasing would be inappropriate? List these situations in the spaces provided.

1. _____

2. _____

3. _____

4. _____

5. _____

6. _____

7. _____

8. _____

9. _____

10. _____

Review your list and you will probably discover that many of your examples refer to situations that are casual, mundane, or ordinary. If someone says to you, "Isn't it a beautiful day?" it would be absurdly comical to reply, "It sounds like you are pleased with the weather." So the use of paraphrasing is not advocated in every interpersonal situation, but rather for more complicated messages when people are describing feelings, emotions, values. When you paraphrase you let other people know you care about what they are saying, and at the same time, you help to avoid confusion and misunderstanding.

## Individual Activity
## Identifying Paraphrasing

For each of the statements given below identify which response is an effective paraphrase of the sender's message.

1. **Speaker:** "Sometimes I think I'd like to drop out of school, but then I start to feel like a quitter."
   **a.** "Maybe it would be helpful to take a break and then you can always come back."
   **b.** "You're so close to finishing. Can't you just keep with it a little bit longer?"
   **c.** "It sounds like you have doubts about finishing school but that you don't like to think of yourself as a person who would quit in the middle of something you started."
   **d.** "What do you think the consequences will be if you drop out?"

2. **Speaker:** "I really don't want to go to a party where I don't know anyone. I'll just sit by myself all night."
   **a.** "You're afraid that you won't feel comfortable starting conversations with people you don't know."
   **b.** "It would really be good for you to put yourself in that kind of a situation."
   **c.** "I can really relate to what you're saying. I feel awkward too when I go to strange places."
   **d.** "Maybe you could just go for half an hour and then you can always leave if you're not having a good time."

3. **Speaker:** "I get really nervous when I talk with people I respect and who I fear might not respect me."
   **a.** "You feel uncomfortable and anxious when you talk with people who you think are judging or evaluating you."
   **b.** "You really shouldn't feel nervous with people you respect because in many ways you are just as good as they are."
   **c.** "I've really found it useful to prepare my remarks in advance. Then I'm not nearly as nervous."
   **d.** "Why do you think you get so nervous around people you respect?"

   **Key:** 1. c; 2. a; 3. a

## Individual Activity
## Paraphrasing: Written Practice

An initial step in helping you to become more comfortable and effective with paraphrasing is for you to begin by writing paraphrase responses. Following you will find six statements. For each statement write a paraphrase that includes both feeling and content. When you are developing your paraphrases, it may help you to recall the formula presented earlier: You feel _____ because
                                                        (feeling)
_____ . Although you will not want to use this formula repeatedly, you can use i
     (event, experience)
as a review to be sure your paraphrase includes both the feelings and content of the other's message

1. **Speaker:** "I just don't know what to do. My parents are coming here from Massachusetts to visit me for a week. They have never been on the West Coast and they are really looking forward to it. But during the time they will be here, I have two mid-terms; plus, they don't know about Mary who is living with me. I know they won't like that."

**Paraphrase:** _____

_____

_____

_____

_____

_____

**2.   Speaker:**   "I'm really starting to hate my job. Every day I do the same boring, mindless work, but I'm afraid if I quit I'll end up unemployed."

**Paraphrase:** _____

_____

_____

_____

_____

_____

**3.   Speaker:**   "This has really been a great day. I passed my comprehensive exams and my husband sent me roses. It feels so good to know that those comps will no longer be hanging over my head. I have spent a lot of hours studying for them, and I feel really good that they are over."

**Paraphrase:** _____

_____

_____

_____

_____

_____

**4.   Speaker:**   "I'm having such a difficult time trying to decide whether or not to put my mother in a nursing home. She dreads the thought and yet she can no longer take care of herself."

**Paraphrase:** _____

_____

_____

_____

_____

_____

**5.  Speaker:**  "My boyfriend is coming over tonight and I'm really worried about what he wants to talk to me about. We haven't been getting along very well lately and I think he might tell me he wants to break up."

**Paraphrase:**  _____
_____
_____
_____
_____
_____

**6.  Speaker:**  "I have been finding out something about myself lately that I don't like very much. When I was living at home my Mom was jealous of my relationship with my Dad. Now I am finding out that I act like she did when my boyfriend goes out with the guys. I guess I am afraid that he likes them better than me."

**Paraphrase:**  _____
_____
_____
_____
_____
_____

## Take-Aways: An Obstacle to Paraphrasing

Sometimes when we are listening, there is a tendency to shift our focus from understanding to agreement or disagreement. In *Alive and Aware*, Miller, Nunnally, and Wackman (1978) call this behavior a *take-away* because it takes the focus of the communicative interchange *away* from the speaker.

If you say, for example, "I feel terrible. I just flunked my history midterm," it would be a take-away if your friend replied, "Oh, I know just how you feel. When I flunked my math midterm, I felt terrible too." Although your friend may have agreed with your perception and provided support and encouragement, the focus of the exchange was still taken away from you. What would an effective paraphrase have been in that situation?

**Paraphrase:** _____

_____

_____

_____

**Individual Activity**
**Identifying Take-Aways in Real Life Situations**

For the next two days, observe people's listening behavior with specific focus on take-aways. On the form provided, describe the speaker's statement and the listener's take-away response. Then write what an effective paraphrase might have been.

| Speaker's Statement | Listener's Take-Away Response | Possible Effective Paraphrase |
|---|---|---|
| **EXAMPLE:** "I'm so confused. I can't decide whether to take a teaching job or go on to graduate school. I should get a real job, but I think I'd really like graduate school." | "Why don't you see if you can get a teaching job first?" | "You're really torn. On the one hand you're thinking that the responsible thing to do would be to get a job. But then graduate school seems real attractive." |

| Speaker's Statement | Listener's Take-Away Response | Possible Effective Paraphrase |
| --- | --- | --- |
| | | |

**Triad Activity**
**Paraphrasing: Some Classroom Practice**

The following two activities have been designed to give you practice paraphrasing. Depending on the amount of time you have available, you may choose to complete both activities, just one, or portions of each. The activities are designed to promote the kind of talk for which paraphrasing is appropriate, meaningful, and helpful.

When you are the speaker, try to give your statements some emotional texture by including descriptions of your feelings. Try doing this activity with three people. Although roles will continually shift, there will be three basic tasks to be performed: speaking, listening, and observing.

**Speaker:**    Make a statement in response to one of the items on the paraphrase activity sheets that follow. Be sure to include both feelings and events where you can.

**Listener:**    Use your own words to communicate what you understand the speaker to be saying.

**Speaker:**    Verify or modify the listener's paraphrased response.

**Observer:**    Provide input to both speaker and listener. What did they do effectively? What could be improved?

Switch roles after each statement. This role switching means that, for every item discussed, each person will be speaker, listener, and observer.

**EXAMPLE:**

**Speaker:**    "I don't believe that love is the key to effective relationships. After all, what is love anyway? I think the key is negotiation and compromise."

**Listener:**    "I agree. Some people get so hung up on the word 'love' that they forget about the day-to-day work that has to get done."

**Speaker:**    "That's not exactly what I mean. I think it's important for people to care about each other, but how can we know what love is apart from a willingness to negotiate and sometimes give in?"

**Listener:**    "It sounds like you're not saying that love is unimportant, but rather that evidence of love is how much people are willing to compromise to help each other satisfy their needs."

**Speaker:**    "That's it."

**Observer:**    "The listener started out with a take-away rather than a paraphrase. Even though you agreed with the speaker you did take the focus away. But I like the way you paraphrased the next statement. You really seem to have gotten the speaker's message."

**Paraphrasing Activity Sheet 1**

1.  When you get right down to it, love is the basis of an effective relationship.

2.  We are who other people tell us we are.

3.  Whenever people speak, they have some purpose or goal they seek to achieve.

4.  People should seek to discover their real selves and avoid changing behavior to fit different situations.

5.  People should spend more time analyzing their interpersonal relationships.

6.  Women are more sensitive and understanding than men.

7.  People should have the right to be silent and unresponsive if they choose to.

8.  Gay partners should be allowed to raise children.

9.  States should be allowed to limit their population growth by placing a limit on out-of-state people who can become citizens of the state.

10.  Persuasion is a necessary component of an effective relationship.

11.  Honesty is vital in a relationship, even if it means inflicting pain.

12.  When you come right down to it, men and women are just not the same.

**Paraphrasing Activity Sheet 2**

1.  I am in college because . . .

2.  At parties . . .

3.  Five years from now I see myself . . .

4.  I feel that the women's movement . . .

5.  Some of my thoughts when I first meet someone are . . .

6.  One thing that I really feel strongly about . . .

7.  In a group of people I usually get most involved when . . .

8.  I would really like to . . .

9.  When I find myself in a new group of people I . . .

10.  Friendship . . .

## Nonverbal Reflecting

Just as paraphrasing gives information about the impact of a message verbally, you can also show your understanding of a message by nonverbal reflecting. To reflect, you mirror the facial expressions and postures of your partner, especially when messages are emotionally charged. For example, you lean toward the partner who leans toward you. If you listen to a friend tell a sad story, your face probably shows a sad expression, too.

You will demonstrate active participation in the nonverbal listening process as you practice nonverbal reflecting. Like paraphrasing, nonverbal reflecting may feel awkward when you first begin, but you will soon find it a comfortable and useful accompaniment to your other listening skills.

---

**Triad Activity**
**Nonverbal Reflecting and Paraphrasing: Extended Practice**

As you practice, you will become more able to paraphrase in difficult interpersonal settings. Paraphrasing is especially useful when your interaction involves negative emotions, because active listening will help alleviate uncomfortable emotional states. Concentrate also on using appropriate nonverbal reflecting while you are paraphrasing.

Each round of paraphrasing activity will take about 7 minutes, with 5 minutes of paraphrasing and 2 minutes of feedback.

**1.** Tell a *personal experience.* Person A paraphrases, B tells the story, and C observes and gives feedback.

**2.** Tell a *problem.* (You may role play a fictitious problem.) Person B paraphrases, C tells the problem, and A observes.

**3.** Give a *criticism.* (Once again, a role play could replace "real" criticism of the partner.) Person C paraphrases, A gives the criticism, and B observes.

**Individual Activity**
**Paraphrasing: Self-Monitoring**

Now describe real life situations in which you could have used paraphrasing but did not. For each of the situations you've described, what would an effective paraphrase have been?

| Situation (Describe Other's Statement) | Paraphrase I Could Have Made |
|---|---|
| **EXAMPLE:**   My friend said to me, "I felt so good to see my sister again. I feel so close with her. Too bad she lives so far away." | "You really value your relationship with your sister and you wish she lived closer so you could be with her more." |

| Situation (Describe Other's Statement) | Paraphrase I Could Have Made |
| --- | --- |
|  |  |

**Perception Checking:
Clarifying Conclusions
About Partner's
Behavior**

*Perception checking* is similar to paraphrasing because it is a receiver behavior designed to clarify the meaning of a sender's message. It differs from paraphrasing, however, because its focus is not limited to the last message uttered by the speaker. Instead, a perception check can refer to behavior over an extended period of time.

Chapter 3 stated that the fundamental purpose of perception checking is to clarify the inferences that we draw about other people's thoughts, feelings, or intentions. We are continuously evaluating, interpreting, and drawing conclusions about the behavior of the people with whom we communicate. Some of you may advocate a nonevaluative mode of responding which would make perception checking unnecessary. If you draw no conclusions, make no interpretations, do not evaluate what others do, then you have no reason to check out your perceptions. This stance seems unrealistic. It is impossible for us to function in daily life without drawing some conclusions about what is happening around us.

The problem, then, is not interpreting, evaluating, or concluding, but rather experiencing those interpretations as reality. If you view your conclusions as inferences needing to be checked out, you then help to prevent the misunderstanding that occurs when you act on your inferences as if they were indeed fact.

---

**Individual Activity
Perception Checking: Identifying a Three-Part Process**

Consider the following examples of perception checking. Each example does three things: (1) describes the sense data from which the conclusion is drawn—that is, what the speaker has seen and heard to lead to the conclusion; (2) describes the inference or conclusion drawn from the sense data; and (3) asks the sender to clarify whether the conclusion is accurate.

Read each statement below and then indicate each of these three functions.

**1.** "When you came into the apartment today and went into your room without saying hello, slammed your door and turned your stereo up loud, I interpreted that to mean that you are angry about something I did. Is that accurate?"

a.  **Sense Data:** _____

_____

_____

_____

**b.  Inference or Conclusion:** _____

_____

_____

_____

**c.  Confirmation Request:** _____

_____

_____

_____

**2.**  "When you didn't respond to my invitation about dinner I thought you really didn't want to come. Is that right?"

**a.  Sense Data:** _____

_____

_____

_____

**b.  Inference or Conclusion:** _____

_____

_____

_____

**c.  Confirmation Request:** _____

_____

_____

_____

**3.**  "You have been very quiet for the last hour and haven't commented on anything I've said. I'm interpreting that to mean that something I've said has bothered you. Is that true?"

**a.  Sense Data:** _____

_____

_____

_____

**b.  Inference or Conclusion:** _____

_____

_____

_____

c.  **Confirmation Request:** _____

_____

_____

_____

---

**Individual Activity**
**Perception Checking: Written Practice**

Following is a list of inferences that one partner in a relationship might make about the other. For each inference, write a perception check that would help to clarify the validity of the conclusion.

**1.**  "You don't seem interested in what I have to say any more."

_____

_____

_____

_____

**2.**  "You really seem tense and uptight tonight."

_____

_____

_____

_____

**3.**  "You are afraid that your parents will disapprove of the way we're living."

_____

_____

_____

_____

**4.**  "You don't seem to feel as close to me as you used to."

_____

_____

_____

_____

_____

_____

**5.** "Why have you been so depressed lately?"

_____

_____

_____

_____

---

**Individual Activity**
**Perception Checking: A Self-Assessment**

Think about the last time you misinterpreted someone else's behavior. Describe the situation. Describe your interpretation. How might a perception check have helped?

**Situation:** _____

_____

_____

_____

_____

**Your Interpretation:** _____

_____

_____

_____

_____

**Possible Perception Check:** _____

_____

_____

_____

_____

_____

**Individual Activity**
**Active Listening: Putting It All Together**

Now try to increase your use of active listening. On the form provided, describe situations in which you were particularly pleased with a perception check or paraphrase you made. Describe the impact of your listening behavior on others.

| Situation (describe other's statement where appropriate) | Active Listening Response (describe specific language you used) | Impact on Other (describe specific behaviors) |
|---|---|---|
|  |  |  |

# 7 Relationships

You only initiate conversation with a small proportion of the many strangers you see every day. And of those that you actually do talk to, you remain continuously involved with a smaller number still. When you consider the fraction of those casual relationships that eventually turn into close friendships, the number is quite small indeed. Why is it that we choose to initiate relationships with some people over others? Why is it that some relationships fizzle out after ten minutes of conversation whereas others become more intense and continue to grow over time? And perhaps the most fundamental question of all: What is it that *you can do* to affect the outcome of your relationships?

Many people believe that relationships are a product of some mysterious, enigmatic attraction. This text, in contrast, takes the position that relationships are explainable—that is, they can be understood, changed, and influenced. Some people think that intentional change will harm relationships. This is simply not the case. By what we say and do, we continually affect the direction of our relationships. The choice is not whether to influence, but whether to work on relationships skillfully or unintentionally.

In this chapter we will look at how relationships are initiated, maintained, and enhanced over time. When you complete this chapter you should be more skilled in initiating communication and establishing contact with strangers and acquaintances. You should also be more effective in maintaining, enhancing, and modifying the relationships in which you are presently involved.

## Establishing New Relationships: Discovering Common Ground

Often at parties, school, meetings, work, and so forth, we find ourselves in the company of people we know nothing about. What can we say to get the conversation started? In many respects conversation can be viewed as the search for commonalities. As we talk, we try to find similar experiences, interests, feelings, or beliefs that we can discuss. Perhaps that is why talking about the weather is so standard—the weather is something that even strangers have in common. To help clarify the importance of common ground, divide the class into equal groups of five to eight people. Then, complete the following task:

Generate as long a list as possible of all the commonalities that the people in your group share: activities that you enjoy, events that you have experienced, objects that you own, hobbies or interests that you have. For this exercise the quality of your commonalities is not as important as the quantity. The only limitation is that your list should not include "never" items. "We have never been to Egypt"; "We have never eaten raw fish." All other commonalities are acceptable. Take about five to ten minutes to complete this part of the assignment.

---

### Small Group Activity
### Group Commonalities

List the commonalities shared by the members of your group. Include activities that you enjoy, events you have experienced, objects you own, hobbies or interests that you have.

1. _____

2. _____

3. _____

4. _____

5. _____

6. _____

7. _____

8. _____

9. _____

10. _____

11. _____

12. _____

13. _____

14. _____

15. _____

16. _____

17. _____

18. _____

19. _____

20. _____

21. _____

22. _____

23. _____

24. _____

25. _____

26. _____

27. _____

28. _____

29. _____

30. _____

31. _____

32. _____

After each group quickly runs through its list of commonalities for the rest of the class, think about how this activity is similar to what you do when you talk to a person for the first time. Obviously, when you initially meet someone you do not sit down with a pencil and paper hurriedly writing all of your commonalities. Even so, how does this activity simulate real initial encounters?

---

## Initiating Conversation: Making the First Move

Establishing common ground is clearly an important aspect of initiating relationships. But before common ground can be established, contact must be made and conversation initiated. Glaser and Biglan (1977) systematically approach the process of initiating conversation through a five step procedure. That procedure, adapted from Glaser and Biglan's *Increase Your Confidence and Skill in Interpersonal Situations*, is described below.

**1.  Look for Approachability Cues**   The approachability cue is an idea originally developed by G. M. Phillips (1972). If someone is buried in books at the library, writing a letter at lunch, or talking intensely with a group of people at a party, you would not consider that person a good choice to approach. To find a more appropriate target, look for *approachability cues*: a person sitting alone at lunch or a party, someone playing with a dog in the park, an individual waiting for a bus or sitting alone in a meeting or class. A smile is often a sign of approachability.

**Individual Activity
Discovering Approachability Cues**

For the next day or two begin to observe approachability cues wherever you go. Use the form provided to record your observations. Describe both the verbal and nonverbal behavior that signifies to you whether or not a person is approachable.

| Approachability Cues | Nonapproachability Cues |
|---|---|
| **EXAMPLE:**   I walked into my dining hall. A woman who was eating alone looked up from her food and smiled at me. | **EXAMPLE:**   I was at my friend's party. Two people were talking to each other, gazing into each other's eyes, and standing very close. |
| 1. _____ | 1. _____ |
| 2. _____ | 2. _____ |
| 3. _____ | 3. _____ |

| Approachability Cues | Nonapproachability Cues |
|---|---|
| 4. _____ | 4. _____ |
| _____ | _____ |
| _____ | _____ |
| _____ | _____ |
| _____ | _____ |
| 5. _____ | 5. _____ |
| _____ | _____ |
| _____ | _____ |
| _____ | _____ |
| _____ | _____ |

**2.  Opening: Introducing Sets**   Learning skills for conversation necessarily includes opening and closing the interaction. Hargie, Saunders, and Dickson (1981) discuss the importance of developing links between the expectations of communicators and what is really going to happen in a communication situation. "Introducing a set" means preparing your listener for what you are about to discuss; you ready the person to understand the information that is to follow. For example, you might remark to your roommate, "You'll never guess what happened to me today," as an introduction to a self-disclosure.

Introducing the set and closure can be especially important in beginning relationships, because you and your new acquaintance have little information about each other. Your listener doesn't know what to expect in interactions with you.

You can practice the verbal and nonverbal elements of social and informational set introduction. Introducing a social set means using nonverbal behaviors such as a handshake to promote a positive tone and affirmative verbal behaviors such as, "Hi, good to meet you." Introducing an informational set means using verbal behaviors that specify your goals for the interaction, such as "I'm new in the dorm and I wanted to meet the people on the hall."

**Individual Activity**
**Monitoring Set Introduction**

This exercise will help you discover which sorts of set introductions you use most often and which you use least often. Use the space provided to monitor your introductory remarks for the next few days.

**EXAMPLE:**

**Situation:**  in Interpersonal class

**Social:**  I smile and remark, "Hi, I'm Anna."

**Informational:**  "I noticed your 'Oregon' shirt and wanted to ask where you got it."

1.  **Situation:** _____

    **Social:** _____

    **Informational:** _____

2.  **Situation:** _____

    **Social:** _____

    **Informational:** _____

3.  **Situation:** _____

    **Social:** _____

    **Informational:** _____

4.  **Situation:** _____

    **Social:** _____

    **Informational:** _____

**3.  Search the Situation for Topics**  Every environment offers its own conversation starters. If you are in a restaurant you can talk about the food, the service, the customers, the decor, the noise level. If you are at a party, you can talk about the music, the plants, the paintings, or your mutual friends. If you are in a classroom, you can talk about the course, the teacher, the homework. *Searching the environment* for topics is usually a good place to begin because your shared environment is one commonality of which you can be certain.

**Individual Activity**
**Beginning a Conversation: Look Around**

On the form provided, describe conversation starters in three different environments. Try to come up with at least three conversation starters for each environment. Remember to presume that you know nothing about the person you are speaking to in each of these situations. You have only the environment to rely on in your topic choices.

**EXAMPLES:**

**Situation:**   waiting in line for a movie

**Topic a:**   How I feel about waiting in a long line.

**Topic b:**   What I've heard about this particular movie.

**Topic c:**   What the weather is like: Is it cold, rainy, or sunny while we are waiting?

**1.   Situation:**   riding in a bus

**Topic a:** _____

_____

**Topic b:** _____

_____

**Topic c:** _____

_____

**2.   Situation:**   visiting a friend's home

**Topic a:** _____

_____

**Topic b:** _____

_____

**Topic c:** _____

_____

**3.   Situation:**   jogging on the beach

**Topic a:** _____

_____

**Topic b:** _____

_____

**Topic c:** _____

_____

**4.   Make Transitions to Other Topics**   Most topics may be used as bridges or *transitions* to other related topics. For example: If you are talking about the food in a restaurant, you might move the conversation by discussing other restaurants in town. If you are at a party talking about the music, you might make a transition by talking about your musical preferences. If you are in a history class discussing the course, you might make a transition to other history courses you have taken. Transitions, then, link the topic you are discussing with other related topics.

## Keeping It Going with Transitions

Return to the topics you generated in the previous activity. Choose five, and use the form provided to develop three possible transitions for each topic.

**EXAMPLE:**

**Topic:**   How I feel about waiting in a long line

**Transition 1:**   The last time I waited in a line this long was to see *Star Wars*. Did you see that movie? What did you think of it?

**Transition 2:**   If you think this is bad, you should try waiting in line in New York where everyone tries to get in front of you.

**Transition 3:**   I have a friend who brings his knitting whenever he expects to wait in line. One time I was waiting in line with him and. . . .

**Topic A:** _____

**Transition 1:** _____

_____

**Transition 2:** _____

_____

**Transition 3:** _____

_____

**Topic B:** _____

**Transition 1:** _____

_____

**Transition 2:** _____

_____

**Transition 3:** _____

_____

**Topic C:** _____

**Transition 1:** _____

_____

**Transition 2:** _____

_____

**Transition 3:** _____

_____

**5. Give and Use Free Information**   When you are getting to know someone you can help them to learn more about you by offering some *free information* when you answer their questions. "Free information" means that, in addition to providing someone with whatever information he or she actually asked for, you will also give related and pertinent information that helps the other get to know you a little better. For example, if someone asks what time you usually leave your office, one response might be: 5:00 P.M. This response has no free information. Another response might be, "I leave my office at 5:00 so I can pick up my daughter at preschool by 5:30." This response does give the other person some additional information, information that has the potential to move your conversation in a new direction.

Free information helps to build a conversation when it is offered and responded to. When we talk to people they usually provide us with more free information than we could possibly use. Yet we often miss it all. Imagine, for example, that you are waiting for the train. You ask a woman what time it arrives. She says to you, "It's scheduled for one o'clock, but we better prepare to wait. This train is usually late." In this example you not only received the information you asked for (the arrival time) but you also received some free information. By saying, "the train is usually late" this person is telling you that she has taken this particular trip with some frequency. That is a topic that you can then discuss.

**Individual Activity**
**Free Information**

During the next two or three days, use the form provided to keep track of the free information you receive and give.

When you *receive* free information record the following data: (1) a description of the other person's statement; (2) the part of the statement that is free information; (3) your response; and (4) your preferred response. (The assumption is that your preferred response makes more effective use of free information than what actually occurred.)

When you *give* free information record the following data: (1) your statement; (2) the free information component of your statement; (3) the other person's response to that statement; and (4) a preferred response to that statement. (Again, the preferred response will make more effective use of the free information than the actual response did.)

## Free Information You Receive

| Other's Statement | Free Information Component | Your Response | Your Preferred Response |
|---|---|---|---|
| **EXAMPLE:** I like Oregon as much as you do, but I do miss the East. | "I do miss the East" suggests that this person has spent some time on the East Coast. | What do you like best about Oregon? (Does not make use of free information.) | Did you live in the East? What did you like best about it? |
|  |  |  |  |

## Free Information You Receive

| Other's Statement | Free Information Component | Your Response | Your Preferred Response |
|---|---|---|---|
|  |  |  |  |

## Free Information You Give

| Your Statement | Free Information Component | Other's Response | Other's Preferred Response |
|---|---|---|---|
| **EXAMPLE:** I really like this sunny weather, too, but I wish I had more time to enjoy it. I've been spending most of my time inside writing. | I've been working actively on some kind of writing project. | I'm glad I've had a chance to go hiking and camping and fishing. (Does not make use of free information.) | What is it you're writing? |
| | | | |

## Free Information You Give

| Your Statement | Free Information Component | Other's Response | Other's Preferred Response |
|---|---|---|---|
| | | | |

**6. Ask Questions** *Questioning* is an excellent way to keep conversations going and to learn more about the people you meet. Questions tend to make people feel that you are actively interested in what they are saying. Glaser and Biglan (1977) discuss these types of questions:

**a.** Open-ended and closed-ended questions: Closed-ended questions have only one-word answers. Usually they begin an interaction or a new subject. Examples might include a yes-no question ("Are you going to school here?"), a selection ("Do you want to hear blues or rock?") or an identification ("Where are you from?").

Open-ended questions invite a wide variety of responses, leaving the choice up to the respondent. Responses to open-ended questions tend to be three times longer than answers to closed-ended ones (Dohrenward, 1965). An example is "How did you happen to come to college here?"

**b.** Broad and focused questions: Broad, general questions offer the maximum amount of response freedom to a respondent. Therefore they may draw a response that is too broad to convey much information. For example, "How was your school year?" may invite the universal "Fine" because of the vagueness of the question.

Focused questions probe for details, examples, impressions, and feelings. The focus that you choose provides direction for the respondent in answering your question:

1. Additional detail.
   **EXAMPLE:**  What was it like to change colleges last year?

2. Specific examples.
   **EXAMPLE:**  What places are good for Italian food around here?

3. Particular impressions.
   **EXAMPLE:**  How do you think this college compares in grading to your old one?

Asking questions increases the probability that you will have more involved and detailed conversations with people. Not only do questions let other people know that you are interested in them but, by asking questions, you become an active participant in the conversation without having to initiate new topics.

**Individual Activity**
**Questioning: Written Practice\***

Read the statements listed below and for each one write an open-ended and a focused question.

**EXAMPLE:**

"I am looking forward to starting school after being away from it all summer."

**Your Question:**    "What are you looking forward to most?"

**1.**   "I really enjoy my job of teaching third graders. In fact, even though it takes a great deal of energy, I don't often think of it as work."

**Your Question:**   _____

_____

_____

**2.**   "We went camping last weekend and it rained from the moment we got there until the moment we left."

**Your Question:**   _____

_____

_____

**3.**   "My boss is really driving me crazy. I have such a hard time saying no to her."

**Your Question:**   _____

_____

_____

**4.**   "Boston is one of my favorite cities."

**Your Question:**   _____

_____

_____

**5.**   "I can't believe how different college is from high school."

**Your Question:**   _____

_____

_____

\*From  Glaser and Biglan, *Increase Your Confidence and Skill in Interpersonal Situations*, Chapter 1.

**7. Closure** Closure is a complementary skill to set introduction; it lets your partner know that the interaction is drawing to a close. Closure can take the form of an ending exchange like "Bye for now" or a statement before the final exchange that acknowledges or sums up the encounter, like "I've enjoyed seeing you again." You can show closure by breaking eye contact or shifting into a new posture.

Verbal statements of closure summarize the encounter or provide social acknowledgment. A *summary* includes feelings and information: "I appreciate your help. Now I understand that the main thing my paper needs is a section on mass media." *Acknowledgment* provides supportive comments about the present meeting and often states a hope for future meetings: "Thanks for the dinner. I hope we can get together again soon."

---

**Individual Activity**
**Closure: Written Practice**

For each of the following situations, provide an example of a closure. Identify whether the closure is a summary or an acknowledgment.

**EXAMPLE:** after my friend's party

**Acknowledgment:** Thanks for inviting me. I enjoyed meeting all your friends from school.

**Situation:** after a study group

_____

_____

**Situation:** after a date you didn't enjoy

_____

_____

**Situation:** after a weekend at your friend's ranch

_____

_____

---

**Dyad Activity**
**Establishing Relationships: Putting It All Together**

Let us review our seven-step procedure for initiating conversations and establishing relationships:

1. Look for approachability cues.

2. Introduce the set.

3. Search the situation for topics.

4. Make transitions to other topics.

5. Give and use free information.

6. Ask questions.

7. Closure.

Now, let's take the opportunity to put it all together. Find someone in your class with whom you have not spoken before. Talk to this person for five minutes. At the end of this time, all talking should cease while each of you records conversational examples that illustrate the seven procedures for initiating and maintaining conversation. After two minutes of writing time you then have three minutes to give this feedback to each other. This is an opportunity for you to discuss the specific conversational strategies that you and your partner used.

It is useful for your instructor to observe some of these conversations and to give specific feedback to the participants. When you have finished this process, find another person in your class with whom you have not yet spoken and repeat the same procedure. The entire process takes ten minutes for each round: five minutes for the conversation, two minutes to write feedback, and three minutes to deliver feedback. At the end of that time, choose a new partner.

### Initiating and Maintaining Conversation: Partner Feedback Form

**Instructions:**    Find examples of each of the following items that helped to maintain your conversation. Also, think of any instances where a particular skill might have been used effectively.

**Situational Topics:** _____

_____

_____

**Free Information:** _____

_____

_____

**Transitions:** _____

_____

_____

**Questions:** _____

_____

_____

**Individual Activity**
**Establishing Relationships: Self-Monitoring**

For the next few days keep a record of conversations in which you could have used situational topics, made transitions to other topics, given or used free information, or asked open-ended, focused questions. The situations that you record might involve friends, acquaintances, or total strangers, and might occur at work, at school, or where you live. Then, write examples of specific conversational procedures that you might have used.

**EXAMPLE:**

**Situation:**   I was eating lunch with a friend in a Greek restaurant. We were seated outside in the courtyard.

1.  Situational topics I might have used:

   **a.**  How comfortable and relaxed I felt to be eating outside in such a quiet place.

   **b.**  My favorite foods at this restaurant: moussaka, psiti, and stuffed grape leaves.

2.  Transitions to other topics I might have made:

   **a.**  Other restaurants in town that I enjoy.

   **b.**  Making Greek food at home.

3.  Free information I might have given or used:

   **a.**  When my friend said, "Greek food is one of the more difficult ethnic dishes to cook," I might have asked her what other ethnic foods she makes.

   **b.**  When my friend asked me how I enjoyed my summer, I might have answered and then added, "But it looks like next summer will be even better."

4.  Open-ended, focused questions I might have asked:

   **a.**  What did you like best about your camping trip?

   **b.**  When you went back East to visit, did you notice any differences in your old friends? Did they notice any differences in you?

## Establishing Relationships: Covert Rehearsal

Have you ever thought about what you would say in a particular communication situation before you arrived? Have you ever practiced how you would ask for the family car to increase the likelihood that you would get it all weekend? Have you ever thought about the words you would use to try to persuade an instructor to change a grade before you actually arrived in that instructor's office? All of these are examples of covert rehearsal: practicing communication behavior in your imagination.

As Chapters 1 and 5 mentioned, covert rehearsal is a skill that, when used effectively, can greatly improve communication in real situations. You may wonder *how* covert rehearsal can be used to establish relationships. How can you practice responding to someone when you have no idea what they will say? How can you practice asking questions or using free information when you don't even know what topics you'll be discussing?

Although some conversational behaviors cannot be prepared in advance, many verbal behaviors can be practiced covertly and used in actual situations. For example, when you go to your speech class, you see the same people every day. You know that if those people were there on Monday, they will probably be there on Wednesday and Friday. It is possible, then, to think about one of those people, and then to covertly rehearse a question that you might ask, some free information that you might give, some situational topics that you might initiate, and even transitions to other related topics. It is possible to covertly rehearse all of this before you get to class. Then when you contact the target person you have a ready store of conversational topics to choose from.

Covert rehearsal is also useful in situations where you think of something to say *after* the situation has passed. If someone offers you free information that you forget to utilize (or if you think of a question about something a person has previously said), it is possible to covertly rehearse your response and then use it when you next see that individual.

---

### Individual Activity
### Covert Rehearsal: Targeting Real People

Here is a chance to practice your covert rehearsal skills. Using the form provided (make more copies if you need to), first designate the person with whom you want to initiate a conversation. Then use the appropriate space to write down *specific* situational topics, transitions, other topics, free information, and questions. As you complete this assignment, remember that covert rehearsal is more than writing down some topics you might initiate. Covert rehearsal is *actually practicing* these kinds of conversational behaviors *in your imagination*, which means that once you've completed a given covert rehearsal form, you then need to take some time to think about it. Actually go through the conversation. During this covert practice you may find changes that you would like to make: additions, deletions, new ideas. Use them!

Each of these assignments on covert rehearsal has two parts. First, you write specific conversational responses. Then, you practice these responses in your imagination.

**Person with whom I want to initiate a conversation:** _____

**Situation:** _____

_____

**Situational Topics:** _____

_____

_____

_____

_____

**Transitions:** _____

_____

_____

_____

_____

**Other Topics:** _____

_____

_____

_____

_____

**Free Information:** _____

_____

_____

_____

_____

**Questions:** _____

_____

_____

_____

_____

### Establishing Relationships in Real Situations

Up to now, considerable time has been spent discussing procedures for initiating conversations and establishing relationships. This information, however, will be of little use unless you actually implement these behaviors in your life. So, after you have spent two days covertly rehearsing conversations with target people, you can begin to initiate these conversations in the actual situations.

Begin with the covert rehearsal situations from the previous exercise that you perceive as most effective. Now implement your imaginal behaviors in real life. When you have completed this practice in the actual situation, take some time to assess what you did. What did you particularly like about your conversational behaviors? How did you establish the contact? How did you help to maintain it? What would you do differently the next time?

## Enhancing Relationships through Discourse

We have all experienced relationships with varying levels of commitment, intensity, and effectiveness. It would be neither desirable nor possible to have an intimate, committed, intense relationship with every person you know. However, it is equally undesirable to have no such relationships.

When two people meet and talk for the first time, anything is possible. They may establish a relationship in which they exchange insults, kisses, lecture notes, or intimate disclosures. In any case, the kind of relationship that is eventually established depends to a large extent on what the participants say to each other. And this is true regardless of whether the people are aware of the impact their discourse is having. Thus, you *can* influence the direction of your relationships.

Talk between good friends is inherently different from discourse between acquaintances. If we can discover some of the basic differences between intimate and casual communication, it will be possible to enhance the quality of our relationships by modifying the characteristics of our talk. In *Alive and Aware*, Miller, Nunnally, and Wackman (1978) describe four different kinds of messages: topic, self, partner, and relationship.

A *topic message* focuses on people, places, or events that are not immediately present. Topic messages refer to all talk that is not about you, your partner, or your relationships. A *self message* focuses on you as a person: your feelings, thoughts, beliefs, experiences. Self messages are reports of experiences that you have had, are currently having, or plan to have. *Partner messages* focus on the feelings, thoughts, experiences of your partner. Both self messages and partner messages have a more personal focus, a more intimate involvement than topic messages. *Relationship messages* refer to discourse about you and your partner as a unit, focusing on the relationship between the two of you. Relationship messages provide evidence that a relationship exists. Perhaps that is why they are the most intimate form of discourse.

**Individual Activity**
**Distinguishing Message Types**

In the following list of statements identify whether the focus of each statement is on topic, self, partner, or relationship.

1. _____ "I had a good time last night at the party."

2. _____ "I really enjoyed that movie."

3. _____ "The television isn't working."

4. _____ "The kids have been impossible today."

5. _____ "The plumber will be over tonight to fix the drain."

6. _____ "Bill was really annoyed with the way his mother had acted."

7. _____ "I hope it is sunny this weekend so I can go swimming."

8. _____ "I feel so happy to be living in Oregon."

9. _____ "What time does the gas station open?"

10. _____ "I'm not sure whether I want to stay in school or get a job."

11. _____ "When do you think you'll finish your paper?"

12. _____ "We've really been getting along well lately."

13. _____ "You seem worried today."

14. _____ "I feel so proud to have run six miles."

15. _____ "Should we spend the weekend alone?"

**Key:** 1. self; 2. self; 3. topic; 4. topic; 5. topic; 6. topic; 7. self; 8. self; 9. topic; 10. self; 11. partner; 12. relationship; 13. partner; 14. self; 15. relationship

**Individual Activity**
**Refocusing Messages to Enhance Relationships**

Now that you are able to distinguish topic, self, partner, and relationship statements, a key question becomes: How can you enhance the quality of a relationship by modifying your discourse? Putting it another way: How can you change your talk to positively affect your relationships? When a relationship has a disproportional number of topic messages, the time you spend interacting does little to increase the level of intimacy. If most of your talk focuses on external topics, you have less opportunity to learn about each other's thoughts, experiences, feelings, beliefs.

Think of a relationship that you would like to enhance, a person you would like to know better. For the next few days keep track of your conversations with this person. Record the topics you discuss on the form provided. After you have made an assessment of the kinds of messages that most frequently occur in this relationship decide on some new message focuses to include. Are most of your messages about external topics? If so, you will probably want to include additional self messages, partner messages, and perhaps relationship messages.

Decide which kinds of messages you wish to increase, and record them in the space provided. Then decide on some specific messages that you might deliver in the context of that particular relationship. If you decide, for example, to increase the frequency of self messages, list three self messages that you might deliver to that relational partner. If you decide to increase the frequency of relational messages, list three relationship messages that you might deliver in the context of that particular relationship.

## Message Focus: Self-Monitoring

For the next few days choose a relationship and monitor the messages exchanged. On the following lines describe some representative examples of messages discussed.

1. _____
_____

2. _____
_____

3. _____
_____

4. _____
_____

5. _____
_____

6. _____
_____

7. _____
_____

8. _____
_____

9. _____
_____

10. _____
_____

How many topic messages did you record? _____

How many partner messages did you record? _____

How many self messages did you record? _____

How many relationship messages did you record? _____

### Changing Message Focus

Based on your observation of messages exchanged in the relationship you are observing, what kinds of messages would you like to increase?

Topic?    Self?    Partner?    Relationship?

For each message focus you would like to increase, write three *specific examples* of messages that you want to deliver to your relational partner.

1. Topic Statements:

   a. _____

   b. _____

   c. _____

2. Self Statements:

   a. _____

   b. _____

   c. _____

3. Partner Statements:

   a. _____

   b. _____

   c. _____

4. Relationship Statements:

   a. _____

   b. _____

   c. _____

## Pleasant Activities: A Factor in Relationship Satisfaction

Weiss, Hops, and Patterson (1973) offer us another way to conceptualize the process of relationship enhancement: frequency of pleasant activities. Functional, satisfying relationships may be differentiated from dysfunctional, unsatisfying ones on the basis of pleasant activities; that is, how often the partners participate in events they find enjoyable.

Pleasant activities are defined differently for different people. Some people enjoy running, bike riding, hiking. Others enjoy picking strawberries, making jam, watching television, or taking a nap. Thus, the concept "pleasant activities" should be defined within the context of a particular relationship. In any case, how satisfied you are with a particular relationship may be directly related to the frequency of pleasant activities you share with your partner.

**Individual Activity**
**Increasing Pleasant Activities**

Think for a moment about an ongoing relationship that you would like to enhance. For the next two days, on the form below, keep track of all pleasant activities that you engage in with the other person. At the end of two days, look over your list, and make a decision about the pleasant activities you would like to increase during the next two weeks.

**Relational Partner:** _____

**Pleasant Activities We Participated in from** _____ **to** _____ .
                                            (date)          (date)

1. _____
2. _____
3. _____
4. _____
5. _____
6. _____
7. _____
8. _____
9. _____
10. _____

**Pleasant Activities I Want to Increase over the Next Two Weeks:**

1. _____
2. _____
3. _____
4. _____
5. _____

## Individual Activity
## Relationship Building: Putting It All Together

The purpose of this book is to teach you ways of *actually changing* your own communication behavior. Thus, you should by now be able to observe ongoing relational patterns, and then to *implement* specific strategies for change. The final project in this chapter is designed to organize this process.

Choose a person with whom you are in an early stage of relationship development. Be sure to choose someone with whom you would like to become closer friends. The following project will give you an opportunity to systematically build and enhance this relationship. Its intent is to improve or change observable behavior.

First, you will *monitor* your relationship with someone for a week to ten days. Then, you will analyze *patterns* in the relationship, and formulate a specific *goal statement* which will include your strategies for change. Next, you will implement those *strategies* for two weeks, and then *assess the effectiveness* of your efforts.

## Phase 1—Monitoring Relational Communication

Here are some areas to think about after a given interaction. It is not necessary to respond to each item. Focus only on those areas that are central to a particular interaction.

Setting?
How initiated?
Topics discussed? Initiated by?
Length of conversation?
Types of messages: topic, self, other, relationship?
Questions?
Pleasant activities?
Conflict? How resolved?
Decisions? How made?

How satisfied were you with this interaction?

Not at all satisfied:    1    2    3    4    5    : Very satisfied

On what was your satisfaction rating based? What would have made you more satisfied?

## Phase 2—Describing Patterns

How often do you interact with this person? How long is an average interaction?
When and where do you interact with this person?
How often do you and this person engage in pleasant activities together?
What are these activities?
What kinds of topics do you talk about most frequently? Who initiates what topics?
What types of messages are exchanged most frequently? Are there any message types virtually absent?
Who does most of the talking? Who asks the most questions? Who offers the most opinions?
Do the two of you have any taboo topics?
What kinds of activities do you do together?
Who decides on the activities?
How are decisions typically made? What areas tend to stimulate conflict? How is conflict usually resolved?

## Phase 3—Developing the Specific Goal Statement

After you review your records and write your assessment of the patterns in the relationship, *describe in observable terms* what you want the relationship to look like:

Do you want to increase the frequency or length of interactions?
Do you see a need to talk about different topics? What topics?
Do you see a need to do different activities together? What activities?
Do you want to meet in a different environment? What environments?
Do you want to change decision making or conflict resolution behavior? What changes do you want to make?

Remember, although this is a relationship change project, the focus will be on *changing your own communication behavior.*

## Phase 4—Deciding on Specific Strategies to Implement the Desired Change

What specifically will you say and do to achieve your goal?
When will you contact this person?
What will you say?
What event(s) or activities will you set up?
What will you talk about when you get together?

## Phase 5—Assessing the Effectiveness of Your Strategies

Did you achieve your stated goals? Why or why not?
What (if anything) changed and why?

If you had the opportunity to do this project over again, what would you do differently?

# 8 Self-Disclosure

When we give personal verbal and nonverbal information, we help other people understand our unique world view. Most frequently, we offer self-disclosive information when we are establishing and developing relationships. In considering when to disclose and what information to give, we have only a few guidelines. Both our own experience and current research tell us that too much disclosure too soon can hinder rather than enhance a growing relationship. People we want to get to know have personal rules on how much self-disclosure they value in relationships, and rarely does anyone value total openness.

On the other hand, most of us prefer to tell too little about ourselves rather than too much. Often we hesitate, even when our listeners indicate that they are ready to learn more about our lives. Some people simply haven't learned how to reveal personal stories. Others fear the consequences of self-disclosure. When you complete this chapter, you will have a clearer understanding of the various degrees of self-disclosure, and you will be more skilled at disclosing information about yourself at a variety of levels.

**Individual Activity**
**Self-Disclosure: An Imaginary Assessment**

This exercise will give you a chance to begin to examine some characteristics of your own self-disclosing communication. Think of two significant people in your life. Imagine you were writing a note to each of them. What important things could you say about yourself or your relationship that you haven't yet shared?

Dear _____

_____

_____

_____

_____

_____

_____

_____

_____

_____

Dear _____

_____

_____

_____

_____

_____

_____

_____

_____

_____

_____

**Individual Activity**
**Avoiding Self-Disclosure**

Why do we fear self-disclosure? What are the risks involved when we disclose information about ourselves? In Chapter 8 of *Interplay*, the following list was presented. Originally developed by Lawrence Rosenfeld to investigate sex differences in reasons for avoiding self-disclosure, this instrument should give you some indication of your reasons for avoiding self-disclosing communication. Simply indicate on a scale from 1 to 5 (1 = almost always; 2 = often; 3 = sometimes; 4 = rarely; and 5 = almost never) the extent to which you use each reason to avoid self-disclosing.

_____ **1.** I can't find the opportunity to self-disclose with this person.

_____ **2.** If I disclose I might hurt the other person.

_____ **3.** If I disclose I might be evaluating or judging the other person.

_____ **4.** I can't think of topics that I would disclose.

_____ **5.** Self-disclosure would give the other person information that he or she might use against me at some time.

_____ **6.** If I disclose it might cause me to make personal changes.

_____ **7.** Self-disclosure might threaten relationships I have with people other than the close acquaintance to whom I disclose.

_____ **8.** Self-disclosure is a sign of weakness.

_____ **9.** If I self-disclose I might lose control over the other person.

_____ **10.** If I self-disclose I might discover I am less than I wish to be.

_____ **11.** If I self-disclose I might project an image I do not want to project.

_____ **12.** If I self-disclose, the other person might not understand what I was saying.

_____ **13.** If I self-disclose, the other person might evaluate me negatively.

_____ **14.** Self-disclosure is a sign of some emotional disturbance.

_____ **15.** Self-disclosure might hurt our relationship.

_____ **16.** I am afraid that self-disclosure might lead to an intimate relationship with the other person.

_____ **17.** Self-disclosure might threaten my physical safety.

_____ **18.** If I disclose I might give information that makes me appear inconsistent.

_____ **19.** Any other reasons: _____

## Advantages of Self-Disclosure

Although self-disclosure involves risks, it also provides advantages in interaction. Hargie, Saunders, and Dickson (1981) describe several of these advantages: (1) reciprocation, (2) shared experiences, (3) opening conversations, and (4) personal knowledge. When weighing whether or not to disclose, you balance advantages and risks.

*Reciprocation* refers to the conversation rule that your listener will usually self-disclose soon after you do. When you feel prepared to talk about your own life, in detail, you encourage your listener to do the same. Conversely, if you reveal several things about yourself and your listener does not reciprocate, you will be less likely to continue self-disclosing. The norm of reciprocation helps you give and receive important information and lets you know whether to continue your own disclosures.

You can demonstrate empathy with your listener by revealing that you have shared experiences. When you have lived through the same experience, especially if it involves strong emotions like grief or joy, you may wish to confide this fact to your friend. Without seeking to turn the conversation to your own needs (see p. 101), you can reassure your friend.

*Opening conversations,* especially if you begin to believe that you would like to know a person, frequently depends on ability to disclose appropriately. You reveal details that describe your uniqueness in an exchange with new acquaintances.

You will benefit in your own self-concept development by disclosing yourself to friends. This important, often overlooked, advantage happens when you become more aware of your own ideas during self-disclosing conversation. The process of formulating and presenting statements about yourself will make the thoughts clearer in your own mind. Thus you can increase your *personal knowledge* in discussions with your friends. You will also have the advantage of knowing more about the inner world of your friends when they reciprocate.

---

### Individual Activity
### Advantages of Self-Disclosure

Describe situations over the next few days in which you benefited from using self-disclosure. Watch for the four advantages self-disclosure can bring.

**RECIPROCATION**

**EXAMPLE:**

**Disclosure:** I told Lyall, "I'm really interested in this election."

**Outcome:** Lyall said, "You know, I am, too. I've been thinking about ways to get involved in the campaign. Why don't we call the party headquarters?"

1. **Disclosure** _____
   _____

   **Outcome** _____
   _____

2. **Disclosure** _____
   _____

   **Outcome** _____
   _____

## SHARED EXPERIENCES

**EXAMPLE:**

**Disclosure:**  I said to Rick, "My Mom's been doing pretty well since Grandma died, but I worry that she doesn't talk to anyone about her sadness."

**Outcome:**  Rick disclosed, "When my Mom lost her mother, it seemed to take a while before she could talk about it. I just let her know I was ready if she wanted to talk."

1. **Disclosure** _____
   _____

   **Outcome** _____
   _____

2. **Disclosure** _____
   _____

   **Outcome** _____
   _____

## OPENING CONVERSATIONS

**EXAMPLE:**

**Disclosure:**  When I'd talked to Joan for a few minutes, I said, "This summer was one of the best vacations I've had. I got to travel all over the U.S."

**Outcome:**  Joan said, "I love to travel, too. I grew up in an Air Force family, and we got to live in so many neat places."

1. **Disclosure** _____
   _____

Outcome _____

_____

2. **Disclosure** _____

_____

Outcome _____

_____

**PERSONAL KNOWLEDGE**

**EXAMPLE:**

**Disclosure:**   I told Robin, "I'm just beginning to work on this, but I believe I need to get involved in a professional women's group. What do you think about AAUW?"

**Outcome:**   Robin said, "I'm surprised to hear you say that; I thought you didn't like organizations. But I've been a member for two years, so I'll tell you my feelings about the group."

1. **Disclosure** _____

_____

Outcome _____

_____

2. **Disclosure** _____

_____

Outcome _____

_____

## Degrees of Self-Disclosure

Many people become intimidated by the concept of self-disclosure, believing that it refers to the revelation of one's intimate thoughts and feelings. While this type of total openness may be appropriate in certain relationships, at certain times, there are other less intimate levels of self-disclosure equally valuable to relational growth. Whatever its content, self-disclosing information reveals that which would otherwise be inaccessible to a listener. This information can take many forms: basic data, preferences, beliefs, and feelings are all legitimate forms of self-disclosure. *Basic data* refer to biographical and demographic information: where you were born, where you went to school, the places you've traveled, your current employment, and so forth. *Preferences* refer to likes and dislikes—what kinds of events and behavior please and displease you. *Beliefs* refer to the thoughts and opinions you hold. *Feelings* are the emotional responses you have to your experiences. Of these four categories, facts (basic data) are the least personal, and feelings the most. This state of affairs does not mean, however, that you should immediately attempt to increase your rate of "feeling" statements in all interactions. Disclosing a barrage of intimate feelings to the person you sit next to in your German class, for example, may be just as inappropriate as disclosing no feelings to an intimate partner.

**Individual Activity**
**Levels of Self-Disclosure: Written Practice**

The following activity is designed to give you some practice self-disclosing on a variety of levels. For each of the following topics write two disclosing responses in each of the four categories just mentioned.

**EXAMPLE:**

**Topic:** School

1.  Basic Data
    **a.** I'm a psychology major at the University of Oregon.

    **b.** I'm getting a teaching certificate so I'll be able to teach social studies.

2.  Preferences
    **a.** I like small seminars so much better than large lecture classes.

    **b.** I went to school summer term this year and I really liked it. It seemed much more relaxed and informal.

3.  Beliefs
    **a.** I believe in affirmative action but I don't think there should be quotas for women and minorities.

    **b.** I don't think instructors should count class participation as part of a person's grade.

4.  Feelings
    **a.** I feel scared when I think about the future. I'm almost finished with four years of college, and I still don't know what I want to do with my life.

    **b.** I feel resentful when I have an instructor who doesn't prepare for class.

**Topic:** My Family

1.  Basic Data
    **a.** _____

    **b.** _____

2. Preferences
   a. _____
   b. _____

3. Beliefs
   a. _____
   b. _____

4. Feelings
   a. _____
   b. _____

**Topic:** Friendship

1. Basic Data
   a. _____
   b. _____

2. Preferences
   a. _____
   b. _____

3. Beliefs
   a. _____
   b. _____

4. Feelings
   a. _____
   b. _____

**Topic:** Sports

1. Basic Data
   a. _____
   b. _____

2. Preferences
   a. _____
   b. _____

3. Beliefs
   a. _____
   b. _____

**4.** Feelings

   **a.** _____

   **b.** _____

**Topic:** Music

**1.** Basic Data

   **a.** _____

   **b.** _____

**2.** Preferences

   **a.** _____

   **b.** _____

**3.** Beliefs

   **a.** _____

   **b.** _____

**4.** Feelings

   **a.** _____

   **b.** _____

---

**Individual Activity**
**Self-Disclosure: Base-Line Monitoring**

This exercise will help you discover which categories of self-disclosure you use most frequently and which you use least often. Use the space provided to monitor your self-disclosure with two different people: a close friend, and a more distant acquaintance. Be sure to choose people you see often so that you can complete this assignment within the next few days.

**EXAMPLE:** Jean

**Situation:** while jogging together

**Basic Data:** "I picked strawberries this morning and then I made jam."
"I just bought a new pair of Nike running shoes."

**Preference Statements:** "I like my new running shoes much better than my others."
"I prefer to get all my school work done in the day so I can relax in the evening."

**Belief Statements:** "I think that schools should emphasize fitness more than they do."
"I don't think people should go into teaching unless they really love kids."

**Feeling Statements:**   "I feel so happy and relieved that the weekend is finally here."
"I feel angry and hurt that Rick didn't return my call."

   Notice that this example includes an equal number of basic data, preference, belief, and feeling statements. This was done to clarify the characteristics of each type of disclosure. It is quite possible that in your own monitoring you will discover more of one type than another.

**CLOSE FRIEND**
**Situation 1:** _____

**Basic Data:** _____
_____

**Preference Statements:** _____
_____

**Belief Statements:** _____
_____

**Feeling Statements:** _____
_____

**Situation 2:** _____

**Basic Data:** _____
_____

**Preference Statements:** _____
_____

**Belief Statements:** _____
_____

**Feeling Statements:** _____
_____

**Situation 3:** _____

**Basic Data:** _____
_____

**Preference Statements:** _____
_____

**Belief Statements:** _____
_____

**Feeling Statements:** _____
_____

ACQUAINTANCE

**Situation 1:** _____

**Basic Data:** _____
_____

**Preference Statements:** _____
_____

**Belief Statements:** _____
_____

**Feeling Statements:** _____
_____

**Situation 2:** _____

**Basic Data:** _____
_____

**Preference Statements:** _____
_____

**Belief Statements:** _____
_____

**Feeling Statements:** _____
_____

**Situation 3:** _____

**Basic Data:** _____

_____

**Preference Statements:** _____

_____

**Belief Statements:** _____

_____

**Feeling Statements:** _____

_____

    Now review your data and describe the self-disclosure patterns you have observed in each relationship. Then establish a behavioral self-disclosure goal for each relationship.

**EXAMPLE:   Self-Disclosure Patterns**

Most of our disclosure was characterized by basic data and belief statements, and many of the data and beliefs disclosed were on the topic of running. There were few feeling statements.

**Goal:**   During the next week I will disclose at least two feeling statements to my friend. Specifically, I will describe my feelings of excitement and apprehension about my new job. I will also tell her how secure and supported I feel in my relationship with her.

**Close Friend Self-Disclosure Patterns:** _____

_____

_____

_____

_____

_____

**Goal:** _____

_____

_____

**Acquaintance Self-Disclosure Patterns:** _____

_____

_____

_____

_____

_____

_____

**Goal:** _____

_____

_____

## Self-Awareness and Self-Disclosure

In *Alive and Aware*, Miller, Nunnally, and Wackman (1978) describe five dimensions of self-awareness: sensing, thinking, feeling, wanting, and doing. Since you can disclose only that information of which you are aware, being able to identify and clarify each of these different dimensions provides you with an increased opportunity to disclose what you know to others.

When you disclose *sense data* you report and describe observations of behavior, either your own or others'. For instance, you might make the following "sense" statement, "I noticed that you've come home late from work two days in a row."

When you share an *interpretation* you describe what you are thinking. It is often difficult for people to report sense data without interpreting it. For example, if you say, "You look angry," you are not merely disclosing your sensations: you are, in fact, interpreting what you see, since "angry" is an inference. What sense data suggest the appearance of anger? Perhaps a loud voice, silence, or tight facial muscles. Since interpretations are your opinions and may be wrong, it is important to be able to distinguish sense data from interpretative data.

*Feelings* are your emotional responses to your interpretations of your sensory experiences. Feelings are such significant components of self-disclosure, that an entire chapter of this book has been devoted to them. When we disclose our feelings to someone, we give them access to our private emotional world. And this kind of disclosure has the capacity to increase relational intimacy.

Disclosing *intentions* means describing what you do or do not want in a particular situation. When you disclose your intentions, you allow other people to understand your actions more fully. For example, if I disclose my intentions by saying, "I want you to pay attention to me at parties," you not only know more about me, but you also have a new way to interpret my past behavior in party situations.

Finally, we can disclose information about our *actions*—what we do. Disclosing information about actions can occur on a variety of levels. You may, for instance, disclose action information when you tell a person where you live, what your major is, or where you went on your summer vacation. You also reveal action information when you tell someone that you yell at your children if they disobey, or that you stutter when you're nervous.

By examining and understanding these five dimensions of awareness, you increase your self-disclosure choices by expanding your range of disclosure options. As you are able to identify more information about yourself, your self-disclosure can become more complete. When you have a more accurate understanding of your senses, thoughts, feelings, intentions, and actions, you can give other people a clearer picture of what's going on inside you.

---

**Individual Activity**
**Self-Awareness and Self-Disclosure: Written Practice**

Each of the following statements discloses one particular dimension of awareness. Identify which self-disclosure skill is being used in each statement.

Descriptions:
**a.** Sense    **b.** Interpretation    **c.** Feeling    **d.** Intention    **e.** Action

**1.** _____ I think that's a good idea.

**2.** _____ I'm worried about this course.

**3.** _____ I saw Jim in my English class today.

**4.** _____ I'm disappointed that you didn't like my work.

**5.** _____ I'd like to talk to you about the household chores.

**6.** _____ I notice you are leaning back in your chair and not looking at me.

**7.** _____ I'm confident I'll do well.

**8.** _____ I'm listening.

**9.** _____ I see you're wearing my ring again.

**10.** _____ I believe that you meant to embarrass me.

**11.** _____ I blush when I'm flattered.

**KEY:**    1-b; 2-c; 3-a; 4-c; 5-d; 6-a; 7-c; 8-e; 9-a; 10-b; 11-e

**Individual Activity**
**Awareness and Disclosure: A Self-Assessment**

Think back to a recent intense experience you had with a friend. Your experience may have been a heated argument or a joyful moment. Answer the following questions about that experience.

**EXAMPLE:**

**Situation:**   I was having a discussion/argument with my intimate partner about whether or not we were going to date other people.

**a.**   What did I sense—see, hear, smell, feel, etc.? I noticed that he made very little eye contact with me. He was also shifting in his chair and moving around a lot, changing record albums, getting a beer, etc. He was also biting his lower lip. I also noticed he was disclosing very little about how he felt about the situation and what he wanted.
     What (if anything) did I tell my partner about my sensations? I didn't disclose any of this sensory information to my partner.
     What (if anything) would I have preferred to tell my partner about my sensations? I would have preferred to describe what I was seeing and how I was interpreting those sensations.

**b.**   What did I think? What interpretations, evaluations did I make? I thought he was very nervous and angry. I interpreted his behavior to mean that he didn't want to date other people, and that he was hurt and angry that I did.
     What (if anything) did I tell my partner about my interpretations? I asked him why he was so angry since we had no exclusive agreement?
     What (if anything) would I have preferred to tell my partner about my interpretations? I would have preferred to be more tentative with my interpretation of anger. I would have liked to present the sense data that I used in my interpretation, and then asked if my interpretation of anger was accurate. I would have preferred not to ask him why he was angry since asking him to justify his feelings seemed to hinder our discussion.

**c.**   What did I feel? What was my emotional response? I felt nervous, misunderstood, pressured and angry that I wasn't "being listened to."
     What (if anything) did I tell my partner about my feelings? The only thing I said about my feelings was, "You really make me mad. You're not listening to me and you haven't understood anything I've told you."
     What (if anything) would I have preferred to tell my partner about my feelings? I would have preferred to describe each feeling individually and then let my partner respond. I wish I hadn't made it seem like my feelings were his fault.

**d.**   What were my intentions? What did I want? I wanted us to work out an agreement where we would both be able to date other people. I still consider our relationship to be special and I wanted him to know that. I wanted this agreement to be acceptable to him, too. I didn't want him to feel pressured or jealous. I wanted us to resolve this problem without feelings of anger.
     What (if anything) did I tell my partner about my intentions? The only intention I disclosed was that I wanted to date other people.

What (if anything) would I have preferred to tell my partner about my intentions? I wish I had told him that I wanted him to feel secure and satisfied with the agreement we reached and that I wanted our relationship to remain strong.

**e.**  What did I do verbally and nonverbally? Nonverbally, I was leaning forward pointing accusingly at him and often yelling my message. Verbally, I was accusing him of being overly possessive, and was demanding that he justify himself.

What (if anything) did I tell my partner about my actions? I said nothing about my actions to my partner.

What (if anything) would I have preferred to tell my partner about my actions? I would have preferred to describe what I saw myself doing and to acknowledge that my actions surely added to the difficulty we were having resolving our problem.

**Situation:** _____

**a.**  What did I sense: see, hear, smell, feel, etc.? _____

_____

_____

_____

_____

What (if anything) did I tell my partner about my sensations? _____

_____

_____

_____

_____

What (if anything) would I have preferred to tell my partner about my sensations? _____

_____

_____

_____

_____

**b.**  What did I think? What interpretations, evaluations did I make? _____

_____

_____

_____

_____

What (if anything) did I tell my partner about my interpretations? _____
_____
_____
_____

What (if anything) would I have preferred to tell my partner about my interpretations? _____
_____
_____
_____

**c.** What did I feel? What was my emotional response? _____
_____
_____
_____

What (if anything) did I tell my partner about my feelings? _____
_____
_____
_____

What (if anything) would I have preferred to tell my partner about my feelings? _____
_____
_____
_____

**d.** What were my intentions? What did I want? _____
_____
_____
_____

What (if anything) did I tell my partner about my intentions? _____

_____

_____

_____

_____

What (if anything) would I have preferred to tell my partner about my intentions? _____

_____

_____

_____

_____

**e.**   What did I do verbally and nonverbally? _____

_____

_____

_____

_____

What did I tell my partner about my actions? _____

_____

_____

_____

_____

What (if anything) would I have preferred to tell my partner about my actions? _____

_____

_____

_____

_____

**Individual Activity**
**Self-Disclosure: Observing Others**

During the next two days listen to conversations around you: in classes, in the dorms, at work, in the dining hall, with friends, with strangers. Describe below the types of self-disclosure statements you hear: sense descriptions, interpretations, feeling descriptions, intention descriptions, and action descriptions. Be sure to provide specific examples. What types of disclosure were most often left out? What types did you hear most frequently?

**Sense Descriptions:**

1. _____
_____
_____

2. _____
_____
_____

3. _____
_____
_____

**Interpretation Descriptions:**

1. _____
_____
_____

2. _____
_____
_____

3. _____
_____
_____

**Feeling Descriptions:**

1. _____
_____
_____

2. _____
_____
_____

3. _____
_____
_____

**Intention Descriptions:**

1. _____
_____
_____

2. _____
_____
_____

3. _____
_____
_____

**Action Descriptions:**

1. _____
_____
_____

2. _____
_____
_____

3. _____
_____
_____

What types of disclosure are usually left out?

_____
_____
_____

**Individual Activity**
**Self-Disclosure and Relational Growth**

Relational growth (or the increase of intimacy and intensity) is related, at least in part, to self-disclosure. If disclosure is absent, relationships have no direction for growth. This circumstance suggests that if we increase our disclosure of feelings, intentions, interpretations, sensations, and actions, we enhance the likelihood of relational escalation.

In each of the following statements, relational growth is unlikely because the speaker is disclosing little self-information. Notice how most of the statements below are phrased in ''you'' or ''it'' language rather than more highly disclosive ''I'' descriptions. Revise each statement to include additional self-disclosure of sensations, feelings, intentions, interpretations, and actions.

**EXAMPLE:**   ''You think I'm stupid.''

**Revised Self-Disclosure Statement:**   I notice that when I make a suggestion to you, you look away and ignore me. I feel stupid when this happens.

**1.**   ''You've got a great sense of humor.''

**Revised Self-Disclosure Statement:**   _____

_____

_____

**2.**   ''My feelings didn't get expressed.''

**Revised Self-Disclosure Statement:**   _____

_____

_____

**3.**   ''You don't care about my hopes and dreams.''

**Revised Self-Disclosure Statement:**   _____

_____

_____

**4.**   ''You're so dogmatic.''

**Revised Self-Disclosure Statement:**   _____

_____

_____

**5.**   ''Don't ever do that again.''

**Revised Self-Disclosure Statement:**   _____

_____

_____

**6.**   ''It seems we are just incompatible.''

**Revised Self-Disclosure Statement:**   _____

_____

_____

**7.**   "You're so cute."

**Revised Self-Disclosure Statement:** _____

---

**Dyad Activity**
**Self-Disclosure: A Reality Check**

One way of checking out your frequency and level of self-disclosure is to find out how much a good friend knows about you. Give the following questions to a friend. How accurately did this person describe you?

**1.**   How do I feel when I am in a new group of strangers? _____

**2.**   What does it take courage for me to do? _____

**3.**   When someone ignores me how do I feel? _____

**4.**   What is one thing that I really like about myself? _____

**5.**   How satisfied am I with my work? School? Our relationship? _____

**6.**   How do I see the future of our relationship? _____

**7.**   What do I spend a lot of time thinking about? _____

**8.**   What am I most afraid of? _____

**9.**   What about you irritates me? _____

**10.**   What do I appreciate about you? _____

How accurate were your friend's responses? Based on how your friend responded to these questions, what aspects of yourself do you tend to disclose most fully? What kind of information are you less likely to disclose? Did any of your friend's responses surprise you? Were there any situations in which your friend knew less about you than you expected? Was the reverse ever true? Write your responses in the space provided.

_____

_____

_____

_____

_____

_____

_____

_____

# 9 Emotions

Feelings and emotions play an important part in our communication with other people as well as in the maintenance of our self-concepts. Chapter 2 discussed several of the internal events which contribute to the image of the self: thoughts, dreams, daydreams, perceptions. Emotional experience and expression also add crucial information to our knowledge of self. Self-awareness includes the development of our abilities to identify and describe the full range of emotional experiences.

In addition to helping us know ourselves better, emotional expression enhances relationships. Dialogue about feelings characterizes relationships in which the participants work together to discover how the relationship is progressing. Talking about feelings allows the development of personalized solutions to relationship problems. Furthermore, when we begin to discuss emotions in new relationships, this form of self-disclosure allows us to clarify the direction of the relationship and build trust.

In Chapter 9, you will develop your skills for communicating feelings clearly and directly. When you complete this chapter, you will also know more about managing debilitating emotions. Handling such feelings promotes a positive self-concept and good communication outcomes.

**Individual Activity**
**Emotion: A Self-Assessment**

There is a wide range of emotions that people can experience and reveal in diverse ways. What kinds of verbal and nonverbal cues do you observe in yourself to let yourself know that you are feeling angry, jealous, loving, or fearful?

Choose five emotions that you have experienced and think about the behavioral cues that alert you to each feeling. To help you with this and other assignments, the list of emotions from *Interplay* has been included here.

| | | | | |
|---|---|---|---|---|
| affectionate | dependent | hopeless | overcontrolled | silly |
| afraid | depressed | hostile | oversexed | sincere |
| alarmed | deprived | humorous | paranoid | sinful |
| alienated | desperate | hurt | passionate | sluggish |
| alone | disappointed | hyperactive | peaceful | soft |
| angry | domineering | ignored | persecuted | sorry |
| anxious | eager | immobilized | pessimistic | stubborn |
| apathetic | easygoing | impatient | phony | stupid |
| appreciated | embarrassed | inadequate | pitiful | suicidal |
| attractive | envious | incompetent | playful | superior |
| awkward | evasive | indecisive | pleased | supported |
| beaten | evil | inferior | possessive | supportive |
| beautiful | excited | inhibited | preoccupied | suspicious |
| bewildered | exhilarated | insecure | prejudiced | sympathetic |
| brave | fatalistic | insincere | pressured | tender |
| calm | fearful | involved | protective | terrified |
| caring | feminine | isolated | proud | threatened |
| closed | flirtatious | jealous | quiet | tolerant |
| comfortable | friendly | joyful | rejected | torn |
| committed | frigid | judgmental | remorseful | touchy |
| compassionate | frustrated | lively | repelled | triumphant |
| competent | generous | lonely | repulsive | two-faced |
| concerned | genuine | lovable | restrained | ugly |
| confident | gentle | loved | reverent | unsure |
| confused | giddy | loving | sad | understanding |
| contented | glad | masculine | sadistic | unresponsive |
| cowardly | grateful | masked | secure | uptight |
| creative | grudging | masochistic | seductive | useless |
| cruel | guilty | melancholy | self-pitying | vindictive |
| curious | gutless | misunderstood | self-reliant | violent |
| cut off from others | happy | needy | sexually abnormal | weary |
| defeated | hateful | old | sexually aroused | weepy |
| defensive | homicidal | optimistic | shallow | wishy-washy |
| dejected | hopeful | out of control | shy | youthful |

| Emotion | Behavioral Cues |
|---|---|
| **EXAMPLE:** anger | a. voice loud, high-pitched |
| | b. teeth clenched |
| | c. body tense |
| | d. heartbeat faster than normal |
| 1. _____ | a. _____ |
| | b. _____ |
| | c. _____ |
| | d. _____ |
| 2. _____ | a. _____ |
| | b. _____ |
| | c. _____ |
| | d. _____ |
| 3. _____ | a. _____ |
| | b. _____ |
| | c. _____ |
| | d. _____ |
| 4. _____ | a. _____ |
| | b. _____ |
| | c. _____ |
| | d. _____ |
| 5. _____ | a. _____ |
| | b. _____ |
| | c. _____ |
| | d. _____ |

**Individual Activity
Monitoring Emotional Expression***

Use the form provided to monitor the emotions in your life and the situations in which they occur.

| Situation: Events Surrounding Emotion | Emotion Experienced | Nonverbal Expression | Verbal Expression | Consequences of Behavior |
|---|---|---|---|---|
| **EXAMPLE:**   I was working on a paper that I had to finish for the next day. In the middle of my writing my neighbor walked in and began to chat. | Impatience; resentment. | I was aware of looking away a lot, looking down at my paper, fiddling with my pen, looking at my watch. | I didn't say much. When my neighbor asked questions, I answered with one word. I asked no questions in return. I said nothing about my paper. | My neighbor stayed for about an hour before I managed to say that I had to go back to my writing. Now I realize that all I had to do was say that I was working on a paper and could talk some other time. |
|  |  |  |  |  |
|  |  |  |  |  |

*From Ronald Adler, *Confidence in Communication*, p. 178.

| Situation: Events Surrounding Emotion | Emotion Experienced | Nonverbal Expression | Verbal Expression | Consequences of Behavior |
|---|---|---|---|---|
| | | | | |
| | | | | |
| | | | | |

| Situation: Events Surrounding Emotion | Emotion Experienced | Nonverbal Expression | Verbal Expression | Consequences of Behavior |
|---|---|---|---|---|
| | | | | |
| | | | | |
| | | | | |

Now review the data you collected on your own emotional behavior over the past few days.

**1.** What emotions do you experience most commonly? In what circumstances, and with what people?

_____

_____

_____

_____

_____

_____

**2.** How frequently do you experience an emotion and not express it verbally? Does this tend to occur in certain situations? With certain people?

_____

_____

_____

_____

_____

_____

**3.** How do people respond to your expressions of emotion?

_____

_____

_____

_____

_____

**4.** Are there certain emotions that you seem not to be experiencing? Not expressing?

_____

_____

_____

_____

_____

_____

## Developing Facilitative Self-Talk

By now you are probably more aware of the impact negative self-statements can have on the way you feel and on how you communicate with others. Yet you are still left with an unanswered question: How can you modify your emotions by altering your self-talk? When confronted with debilitating thoughts, you can first ask yourself whether there is any factual basis for the self-statement you are making. If the answer to this question is "yes"—and it may be—you then have the options of problem solving and covert rehearsal.

If, for example, you say to yourself, "You really behaved insensitively toward Ann," you first need to evaluate whether, in fact, you did engage in behaviors that may have been insensitive. If you believe you have so behaved, you can then begin thinking about ways to deal with what you have done. What shall you do? How shall you now behave to rectify this situation? Being in a *problem solving* mode means that you are thinking about possible solutions and alternatives. You may think, for example, about what you want to say the next time you run into your friend. You may consider calling her or going over to see her. You may think about questions you want to ask, statements you want to make, or feelings you want to describe. The important point is that you are not just ruminating and worrying about an event; you are thinking about what to do, and planning a course of action.

If you decide that there is some factual basis for your negative self-talk, you have one other choice: *covert rehearsal*. Covert rehearsal means that you can use your imagination to rehearse the specific communication behaviors you want to utilize in resolving the problem. This technique is most effective when you imagine a variety of alternative communication behaviors. Doing so gives you an opportunity to select what you perceive to be the most effective communicative choices. Covert rehearsal also increases the likelihood that, when you are in the actual communication situation, you will be well prepared.

To summarize, then, if you observe your negative self-verbalizations and believe that they are factually based, you have two facilitative options: problem solving and covert rehearsal. It is equally possible, however, that in evaluating your negative self-talk you arrive at the conclusion that your debilitating thoughts are not factually based. In this situation you again have two cognitive strategies: thought stopping and coping monologues.

*Thought stopping* is a covert procedure by which you gain control over (as well as stop) both worry and negative self-statements. When confronted with negative self-talk, you can *imagine* a loud, aggressive, and unpleasant voice yelling: STOP! Take a moment to imagine such a voice. Were you able to hear it? Now take a few minutes to engage yourself in negative self-statements. Tell yourself how poorly you behaved in some social situation, how inelegantly or inappropriately you confronted someone, how ineffectively you expressed your feelings or opinion. Really give it to yourself covertly. Let yourself have it for behaving so poorly. After you have ruminated for about sixty seconds, think: STOP! For many of you this will halt your internal dialogue. If your dysfunctional thoughts continue, again imagine a loud, aggressive, unpleasant voice yelling: STOP! This time try sustaining the STOP! or repeat it several times.

When you have successfully ceased your negative self-statements, it is then helpful to substitute alternative coping monologues. *Coping monologues* involve the systematic use of certain self-verbalizations. They may be reminders of irrational myths or more logical alternatives. A coping monologue, for example, might go like this: "I feel badly that Ann may have perceived my behavior to be insensitive. But this is not a catastrophic situation. I'm sure there is something I can do about it. Besides, it is unreasonable to think I can be loved by all people at all times. I'm sure there will be many times when people disapprove of what I do. That is something that I just have to learn to live with."

To summarize, if we observe our internal monologues to be unreasonably negative, we may engage in thought-stopping and coping monologues. The chart presented here illustrates (in abbreviated form) covert options for coping with negative self-statements.

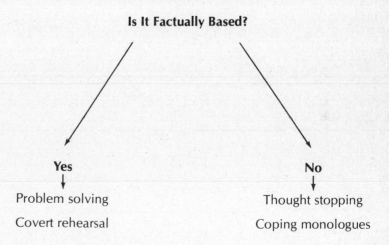

**Negative Self-Talk**

**Is It Factually Based?**

| **Yes** | **No** |
|---|---|
| Problem solving | Thought stopping |
| Covert rehearsal | Coping monologues |

**Individual Activity**
**Converting Negative Self-Talk**

This exercise will now give you an opportunity to practice converting negative self-talk into more facilitative internal dialogue. Consider the following negative self-verbalizations. For each statement write one example of a problem solving statement, covert rehearsal, and coping monologue.

**EXAMPLE:**  I don't know anyone at this party and I can't think of anything to say to anybody.

**a.  Coping Monologue:**  I've only been here fifteen minutes and it's not surprising that I'm still somewhat nervous. I'm sure there are other people here who also don't know anyone and are feeling somewhat uncomfortable.

**b.  Problem Solving Statement:**  I think the best thing I can do now is to approach someone who is sitting alone and initiate conversation. The woman sitting on the rocking chair seems like a good possibility. I'll go over and talk to her.

**c.  Covert Rehearsal:**  I can start by asking her how she got to this party. Maybe we know the same person and can talk about our mutual friend. If not, I can talk about my feelings about going to large parties where I don't know anyone.

**Statement 1:**  I made such a fool of myself on my date with Bonnie. I know she'll never want to go out with me again.

**a.  Coping Monologue:** _____
_____
_____

**b.  Problem Solving Statement:** _____
_____
_____

**c.  Covert Rehearsal:** _____
_____
_____

**Statement 2:**  I can't believe my husband is going fishing again. He just doesn't care at all about me or the kids.

**a.  Coping Monologue:** _____
_____
_____

**b.   Problem Solving Statement:** _____
_____
_____

**c.   Covert Rehearsal:** _____
_____
_____

**Statement 3:**   It's Saturday night and again I have nothing to do. I'm a real loser. No wonder no one wants to spend time with me.

**a.   Coping Monologue:** _____
_____
_____

**b.   Problem Solving Statement:** _____
_____
_____

**c.   Covert Rehearsal:** _____
_____
_____

**Statement 4:**   I'm a terrible daughter. My parents wanted to visit me this weekend and when I told them about how much work I had to do they decided not to come. I feel so guilty.

**a.   Coping Monologue:** _____
_____
_____

**b.   Problem Solving Statement:** _____
_____
_____

**c.   Covert Rehearsal:** _____
_____
_____

**Statement 5:**   My neighbor is so insensitive. His stereo is always too loud for me to study and I've sure dropped enough hints about it. I don't know why I can't get through to him.

a.   **Coping Monologue:**   _____

_____

_____

b.   **Problem Solving Statement:**   _____

_____

_____

c.   **Covert Rehearsal:**   _____

_____

_____

**Individual Activity**
**Monitoring Private Events**

During the next week record every unhelpful, debilitating emotion you experience. Then, for each of these dysfunctional feelings, describe the activating event, and any irrational beliefs or negative self-talk operating.

Next, develop a more facilitative, rational thought or belief to substitute in the chain. In this step you may use any or all of the covert procedures discussed in this chapter: problem solving, covert rehearsal, thought stopping, coping monologues. Use the chart provided to record this information.

| EXAMPLE 1: Debilitating Feeling | Activating Event | Irrational Thought or Belief; Negative Self-Talk | Facilitative Self-Talk | |
|---|---|---|---|---|
| Nervous. | Talking with a guy I would like to date. | I sound so stupid. I can't think of anything to say. He'll never ask me out. | STOP! This is an exaggeration. I might not be perfect, but I'm not stupid. I'm behaving like a nervous woman around a man I'd like to date. I'm not sure what to say, so I'll search the environment for topics. Maybe he'll ask me out. I'll be happy if he does. If he doesn't, I'll be disappointed, but it won't be catastrophic. | [thought-stopping] [coping monologue] [problem solving] [coping monologue] |

| EXAMPLE 2: Debilitating Feeling | Activating Event | Irrational Thought or Belief; Negative Self-Talk | Facilitative Self-Talk | |
|---|---|---|---|---|
| Guilty; embarrassed. | Arguing with my best friend about the guy she's been dating. | I can't believe I told her that her boyfriend was a sexist creep. After all, he is her friend and not mine. It's none of my business who she has a relationship with. I should have kept my mouth shut. | I guess I did say some Inappropriate things to my friend. Now, what can I do about it? I think I'll invite her over for dinner and then I can straighten everything out. Now, what do I want to tell her? I'll say that I feel guilty and embarrassed for mouthing off about her friend. I'll tell her that even though my behavior was inappropriate, I care about her very much. | [problem solving] [covert rehearsal] |

| Debilitating Feeling | Activating Event | Irrational Thought or Belief; Negative Self-Talk | Facilitative Self-Talk |
|---|---|---|---|
| | | | |

Review the data you have collected on your covert behavior. What patterns did you discover? Did the debilitating chain occur more frequently with specific people? Certain types of individuals? Particular settings? Certain topics of conversation?

**Covert Behavior Patterns:** _____

_____

_____

_____

_____

_____

_____

_____

_____

_____

_____

_____

_____

_____

_____

_____

**Individual Activity**
**Positive Self-Talk: Increasing Self-Praise**

Many people are reluctant to praise themselves. We are taught from early childhood that self-praise is egotistical, boastful, lacking in humility. Therefore, our covert behavior tends to focus more on our negative acts than on what we do well.

For the next few days, keep track of all those times that you were pleased with something you did. Remember you can be pleased about a small act as well as an important experience. On the form provided list five to ten things you did that pleased you. Next to each action check whether or not you engaged in positive self-talk as a result of the act. If you did, describe the self-statement in the space provided. If you did not, write an appropriate example of self-praise that you *might have given* yourself.

| Action That Pleased Me | Positive Self-Talk Given? | Self-Praise Statement |
|---|---|---|
| **EXAMPLE 1:** I saw a friend of my brother's in the supermarket. Even though he didn't see me I went up to him and started a conversation. | Yes ☒ No ☐ | Good for me. I really like the way I took the initiative. I could have simply ignored him but I went out of my way to start a conversation. Good going. |
| **EXAMPLE 2:** I was instrumental in resolving a conflict with my sister about using the family car. I explained my position clearly without getting angry or hostile. | Yes ☐ No ☒ | I can really be proud of myself. So many of our car arguments turn out to be fighting matches, but not this time. I really like the way I stayed calm, described my feelings, and explained why having the car was so important to me this weekend. I feel so good about my relationship with my sister now. |
| **1.** _____ | Yes ☐ No ☐ | _____ |
| **2.** _____ | Yes ☐ No ☐ | _____ |

| Action That Pleased Me | Positive Self-Talk Given? | Self-Praise Statement |
|---|---|---|
| **3.** _____ | Yes ☐   No ☐ | _____ |
| _____ | | _____ |
| _____ | | _____ |
| _____ | | _____ |
| _____ | | _____ |
| _____ | | _____ |
| _____ | | _____ |
| _____ | | _____ |
| _____ | | _____ |
| **4.** _____ | Yes ☐   No ☐ | _____ |
| _____ | | _____ |
| _____ | | _____ |
| _____ | | _____ |
| _____ | | _____ |
| _____ | | _____ |
| _____ | | _____ |
| _____ | | _____ |
| **5.** _____ | Yes ☐   No ☐ | _____ |
| _____ | | _____ |
| _____ | | _____ |
| _____ | | _____ |
| _____ | | _____ |
| _____ | | _____ |
| _____ | | _____ |

| Action That Pleased Me | Positive Self-Talk Given? | Self-Praise Statement |
|---|---|---|
| 6. _____ | Yes ☐   No ☐ | _____ |
| _____ | | _____ |
| _____ | | _____ |
| _____ | | _____ |
| _____ | | _____ |
| _____ | | _____ |
| _____ | | _____ |
| _____ | | _____ |
| _____ | | _____ |
| _____ | | |
| 7. _____ | Yes ☐   No ☐ | _____ |
| _____ | | _____ |
| _____ | | _____ |
| _____ | | _____ |
| _____ | | _____ |
| _____ | | _____ |
| _____ | | _____ |
| _____ | | _____ |
| _____ | | _____ |
| _____ | | |
| 8. _____ | Yes ☐   No ☐ | _____ |
| _____ | | _____ |
| _____ | | _____ |
| _____ | | _____ |
| _____ | | _____ |
| _____ | | _____ |
| _____ | | _____ |
| _____ | | _____ |
| _____ | | _____ |

How many times did you actually engage in positive self-talk? Try to increase this rate over the next week. After that try to maintain your rate of self-praise at a level that is reasonable, appropriate, and pleasing.

## Sharing Feelings: When and How

It is important to recognize that your feelings belong to you. Many of us were taught and conditioned to repress feelings. If that was impossible, we were then told to keep them hidden: don't be so upset, don't cry, you shouldn't get so angry, you're too sensitive. And so we learned to express our feelings indirectly, remaining ambiguous enough to feel safe. Sometimes we give ourselves good reasons for not wanting to express our feelings. And sometimes our reasons are legitimate—not everything we think and feel is appropriate to communicate. But even though some degree of covert editing is functional, it is still critical to be able to state feelings clearly and unambiguously.

Few people would argue with this position. Yet few people actually practice it. There are many reasons for the "lack of feeling" descriptions in human interaction. Let's take the opportunity now to arrive at some of these reasons.

## Small Group Activity
### Reluctance to Express Feelings

In groups of five to seven brainstorm a list of reasons people have for not wanting to express feelings. Use the form provided to record the reasons your group describes.

**EXAMPLE:** I didn't want to give him the satisfaction of seeing me upset.

1. _____
2. _____
3. _____
4. _____
5. _____
6. _____
7. _____
8. _____
9. _____

10. _____

11. _____

12. _____

13. _____

14. _____

15. _____

## Accepting Responsibility for Your Feelings

This chapter earlier presented the argument that others do not cause our feelings—we are responsible for the way we choose to react to situations. By becoming responsible for our own emotions, by owning our feelings, our communication becomes less threatening to other people. This means that rather than saying, "You really make me mad," a self-responsible "feeling" description might be, "I feel angry when you say you'll stop by and then don't show up or call."

We can accept responsibility for our own feelings by describing them directly or through analogy. In both of these cases the responsibility for the emotion is accepted by the speaker. Consider the examples:

| Indirect Accusatory | Direct Expression | Expression Through Analogy |
|---|---|---|
| **1.** "Stop trying to control me." | "I feel trapped." | "I feel like the walls are closing in on me." |
| **2.** "You've been so insensitive to my needs." | "I feel confused and frightened." | "I feel like an abandoned child." |

In both direct and analogical expression of feelings, the speaker begins with the pronoun "I" and accepts responsibility for the emotions described. The indirect accusatory expressions, on the other hand, project the responsibility for the emotion onto the other person. This distinction is important. By owning your own emotions with the pronoun "I," you help your listener to receive what you say. In addition, "I" statements are, in fact, a more accurate description of events. You are the expert on your own feelings. The relationship between the other person's behavior and your feelings is far less certain.

**Individual Activity**
**Feeling Descriptions: Written Practice**

Read the following opinions, evaluations, questions, and "you" statements, and change each one into a responsible "feeling" description. Before you begin this activity you may want to refer to the list of feeling words at the beginning of this chapter (see page 166).

**EXAMPLE:**   "You have no right to say that about me."

**Feeling Description:**   "I feel embarrassed and incompetent when you tell people that I have no control over our children."

**1.**   "You shouldn't work late so often. You seem to care more about your job than me."

**Feeling Description:** _____

_____

_____

_____

**2.**   "We have such a good time together."

**Feeling Description:** _____

_____

_____

_____

**3.**   "Can't you ever be on time for an appointment?"

**Feeling Description:** _____

_____

_____

_____

**4.**   "That was a wonderful evening."

**Feeling Description:** _____

_____

_____

_____

**5.** "That was really thoughtless of you to make plans without consulting me first."

**Feeling Description:** _____

_____

_____

_____

**6.** "This whole situation is overwhelming."

**Feeling Description:** _____

_____

_____

_____

**7.** "You are an enjoyable person to be around."

**Feeling Description:** _____

_____

_____

_____

**8.** "You are very rude."

**Feeling Description:** _____

_____

_____

_____

---

**Feeling Descriptions: An Assignment**

Describe a recent situation in which you disclosed your feelings indirectly using opinions, evaluations, questions, or "you" statements. Now, translate this into a responsible feeling description.

**Indirect Statement:** _____

_____

_____

**Feeling Description:** _____

_____

_____

**Individual Activity**
**Monitoring Unowned Feeling Descriptions**

For the next three days keep track of all the feeling descriptions you hear in which the responsibility for the feelings is not accepted by the speaker. You may include examples in which you were either the speaker or the listener. You may also include examples in which you were an outside observer. Then, for each example, write what you would consider to be a more effective alternative, a feeling description that is owned by the speaker.

| Unowned Feeling Description | Responsible Alternative |
|---|---|
| **EXAMPLE:**  "You never include me in your plans." | "I feel abandoned when you go places with your family and don't include me in your plans." |
| 1. | 1. |
| 2. | 2. |
| 3. | 3. |
| 4. | 4. |
| 5. | 5. |
| 6. | 6. |

| Unowned Feeling Description | Responsible Alternative |
|---|---|
| 7. _____ | 7. _____ |
| _____ | _____ |
| _____ | _____ |
| 8. _____ | 8. _____ |
| _____ | _____ |
| _____ | _____ |
| 9. _____ | 9. _____ |
| _____ | _____ |
| _____ | _____ |
| 10. _____ | 10. _____ |
| _____ | _____ |
| _____ | _____ |

## Timing: Deciding When to Share Feelings

Have you ever been writing a paper, studying for a test, or getting ready to sleep when a friend wants to talk about feelings? You may have felt obligated to listen, and yet you were probably frustrated because of your friend's bad timing. What did you do in this situation? How did you feel?

Timing is an important component of sharing feelings effectively. If the receiver of your message is busy, tired, distracted, upset, it is probably not the best time to describe your feelings.

**Individual / Group Activity**
**Timing: A Self-Assessment**

Think for a moment about yourself as a receiver of feeling statements from other people. When are some of your good times for hearing about peoples' feelings? When are some of your bad times? List these times on the form provided. Then, in groups of five to seven people, discuss the issue of timing. Did any of the same situations of good or bad timing occur on several lists? What can you now say about the relationship between timing and sharing feelings?

**For Me, Some Good Times for Receiving Feeling Statements Are:**

1. _____

_____

2. _____

_____

3. _____

_____

4. _____

_____

5. _____

_____

_____

**For Me, Some Bad Times for Receiving Feeling Statements Are:**

1. _____

_____

2. _____

_____

3. _____

_____

4. _____

_____

5. _____

_____

_____

_____

**Individual Activity**
**Feeling Descriptions: Self-Monitoring**

For the purpose of this assignment choose a particular person (Jim) or a category of people (sorority sisters) with whom *you would like to increase your rate of feeling statements*. Begin by observing and recording those situations where you could have described your feelings but did not. These situations will be ones in which you did experience a feeling but did not communicate it to the other person.

| Description of Situation | Feeling Statements I Might Have Made, but Didn't |
|---|---|
| **EXAMPLE:**   I spent an evening with my friend Lynne. We had dinner together and then we talked for hours. When I left, I felt extremely pleased about our relationship but I didn't say anything to Lynne. | "I feel so comfortable and secure with our relationship, Lynne. I feel really appreciated when I'm with you and I want you to know that." |
| **EXAMPLE:**   Lynne and I had plans to go to the coast on Sunday. She cancelled those plans when a guy from her karate class asked her to go on a picnic with him. | "I feel rejected and jealous when you break plans with me to spend time with a guy." |
| 1. _____ | 1. _____ |
| 2. _____ | 2. _____ |
| 3. _____ | 3. _____ |

| Description of Situation | Feeling Statements I Might Have Made, but Didn't |
|---|---|
| 4. _____ | 4. _____ |
| _____ | _____ |
| _____ | _____ |
| _____ | _____ |
| _____ | _____ |
| 5. _____ | 5. _____ |
| _____ | _____ |
| _____ | _____ |
| _____ | _____ |
| _____ | _____ |
| 6. _____ | 6. _____ |
| _____ | _____ |
| _____ | _____ |
| _____ | _____ |
| _____ | _____ |
| 7. _____ | 7. _____ |
| _____ | _____ |
| _____ | _____ |
| _____ | _____ |
| 8. _____ | 8. _____ |
| _____ | _____ |
| _____ | _____ |
| _____ | _____ |
| _____ | _____ |

| Description of Situation | Feeling Statements I Might Have Made, but Didn't |
|---|---|
| 9. _____ | 9. _____ |
| _____ | _____ |
| _____ | _____ |
| _____ | _____ |
| _____ | _____ |
| 10. _____ | 10. _____ |
| _____ | _____ |
| _____ | _____ |
| _____ | _____ |
| _____ | _____ |

When you have completed the monitoring portion of this assignment, you are ready to begin covert rehearsal of feeling descriptions. Think of five different feeling statements you could make to your target person(s). Remember, these feeling statements may be positive or negative, but they should always be in a self-responsible form.

In the spaces provided, write five possible feeling statements that you might give your target person(s). All five statements may be directed to the same individual, or you may have a number of different people as targets. For the next day or two covertly rehearse these statements—really imagine yourself describing these feelings to the other person. And think about the other person responding to you.

Evaluate your various covert attempts at feeling descriptions. Then choose one that particularly pleases you to give in an actual situation.

**Target Person:** _____

**Feeling Description:** _____

_____

_____

_____

_____

_____

_____

**Target Person:** _____

**Feeling Description:** _____

_____

_____

_____

_____

_____

**Target Person:** _____

**Feeling Description:** _____

_____

_____

_____

_____

_____

**Target Person:** _____

**Feeling Description:** _____

_____

_____

_____

_____

_____

**Target Person:** _____

**Feeling Description:** _____

_____

_____

_____

_____

_____

# 10 Communication Climate

A communication climate is the pervasive mood of a relationship. It encompasses many of the behaviors and ideas we have discussed so far. When you think back to the early chapters, you will realize that the climate varies from system to system. Some systems, like a close friendship, feel warm and sunny, whereas others seem to threaten stormy outbursts.

Climate grows from the day-to-day behavioral and perceptual patterns you and other people bring to the system. You and the people with whom you interact have the ability to influence the kind of climate you build in your communication systems. Your effectiveness in any particular system may depend, to a large extent, on the climate you have developed and maintained.

When you complete this chapter, you will have a clear understanding of how communication relates to climate in a system. You will practice sending and receiving information in ways that initiate and enhance a positive climate in your important communication systems. You will learn more about complimenting, positive attention, stating opinions provisionally, and criticism.

## Initiating and Maintaining Positive Communication Climates

In Chapter 10 of *Interplay* you learned that a communication climate is affected by the degree to which people see themselves as valued. The climate is apt to be sunniest when people perceive their relational partners to be concerned about their welfare. If you believe that your friend is concerned about what happens to you, and your friend feels the same way, it is more likely that a positive communication climate will exist in your relationship. The task then becomes to discover which communication behaviors encourage individuals in a relationship to feel valued.

## The Gift of Paying Attention

When a person you are talking with introduces a topic, the communication climate is affected by the way you respond. If you attend to the other's topic by asking a question, making a comment, agreeing or even disagreeing, you are suggesting that what this person has to say is valuable and worth talking about. On the other hand, when you fail to address a topic initiated by another, such nonattending behavior may be interpreted to mean disinterest, boredom, or lack of concern. The other is likely to feel less valued, thus making the interpersonal climate more tenuous.

The communication climate is influenced by nonverbal behavior as well. When you listen to someone speak, you can be encouraging by providing conversation maintainers, content-free verbalizations that suggest you are actively attending to what the speaker is saying. Phrases such as "ahum," "hmmm," "oh, I see," "yes, go on" help the speaker to feel listened to. These conversation maintainers are useful when you want to acknowledge the speaker's message without interrupting the flow of discourse.

---

### Triad Activity
### Personal Attention: Some Practice

This activity should be done in groups, consisting of two participants and one observer. Roles are to be continuously shifted so that each person has an equal opportunity to be both participant and observer. One participant should think of an experience, event, or story to relate to the other. Throughout this process an attempt should be made to engage in a high frequency of personal attending behaviors: questions, comments, agreement, disagreement, conversation maintainers.

Observers should take notes on the frequency of these communication behaviors. Then, at the conclusion of a five to ten minute conversation, observers share their data with the participants. It is helpful to provide specific suggestions about places where personal attention might have been increased.

### Small Group Activity
### Responding to Others' Messages

This assignment is to be done in groups of four or five. The task of each group over the next three days is to observe and record instances of interpersonal responses that are likely to: (a) enhance, or (b) discourage a positive communication climate. The form provided should help you to organize and record your observations. Make copies of the form as you need them.

Within each group individuals may function in pairs or alone. You may observe your own behavior, each other's behavior, the behavior of friends and even the behavior of strangers you see in the cafeteria, student union, parties, classes, or at work. At the end of three days share your findings with each other. Then present an edited version to the class.

**EXAMPLE:**

**Situation:**   I was eating in the school cafeteria and heard this conversation between two people sitting at my table.

**Topic Initiated:**   One friend said to the other, "I'm really feeling uptight and confused about my future. I've spent the last four years majoring in anthropology, and now what can I do with my life?"

**Questions:**   None.

**Comments:**   The other replied, "You're not the only one in that situation. I know quite a few people who say the same thing. I think maybe I'll go to graduate school."

**Agreement:**   None.

**Disagreement:**   None.

**Your Assessment of the Effect of These Behaviors on the Communication Climate:**   These behaviors seem to have had a negative impact on the communication climate. The speaker still seemed upset and concerned, but didn't say anything else. Maybe the speaker felt put-down by comments like, "You shouldn't worry about it so much . . . you're not the only one."

The listener could have created a more positive climate by first asking questions to find out how the speaker was feeling and perhaps help to resolve the problem. For example, "What are some of the work possibilities for anthropology majors? Would you be able to support yourself? Is your family going to give you a hard time?" Agreement statements would have also helped. The listener could have at least agreed that the speaker's situation was a difficult one to be in.

**Situation:** _____

_____

**Topic Initiated:** _____

_____

_____

**Questions:** _____

_____

_____

**Comments:** _____

_____

_____

**Agreement:** _____

_____

_____

**Disagreement:** _____

_____

_____

**Your Assessment of the Effect of These Behaviors on the Communication Climate:** _____

_____

_____

_____

_____

_____

_____

_____

_____

**Complimenting:
Validating the Other's
Assets**

When you compliment someone you are explicitly affirming the ways in which you appreciate that person. Even though our culture teaches us the virtues of humility, most people like to receive compliments. In fact, research suggests that our liking for people is heightened if they compliment us. This is not to suggest that you should engage in insincere flattery. However, if you genuinely admire or appreciate something about another person, expressing it will help you to establish and maintain a positive communication climate. If you do not compliment people they may not realize that you feel positively about them. And if they do not see themselves as valued by you, the likelihood of a positive climate is greatly reduced.

Glaser and Biglan (1977) provide a detailed description of the process of complimenting. The major points of their discussion are included here. A compliment is a positive statement about another person's behavior, appearance, or possessions. Compliments are particularly appropriate when people do things that please you, or when you admire something about an individual. You can also compliment someone by telling a third party something favorable about that person. For example, if you were with two friends, Jean and David, you might compliment Jean by telling David the following: "You should have seen Jean in class today. She disagreed with Dr. Johnson in such a clear and organized way. She really sounded sophisticated and intelligent." By giving a compliment in this way, you say something commendatory about someone and at the same time open up a new area of conversation. When one person tells you something positive about another, you can be a "compliment messenger" by relaying that praise to the person involved. Here are two examples:

"Pat said that you are a really fine guitarist. I didn't even know that you played the guitar. Have you ever taken lessons?"

"Judy and I were talking last night and she told me you were the most considerate roommate she has ever had. That must make your living situation very comfortable for both of you."

By being a compliment messenger you let the person you compliment know about the positive things that other people say. Compliments, just like other communication behaviors, can be enhanced if you use the person's name. This can make the communication climate more personal and, especially with new relationships, can help people feel attended to and valued.

**Individual Activity**
**Validating the Other's Assets: Written Practice\***

Read the description of each situation below. Then write a compliment that you think would help to create a positive communication climate.

**EXAMPLE:**   You had to miss class and a friend lent you notes that were well organized and helpful.

**Your Compliment:**   "Thanks so much for lending me your notes. They seemed so clear. I think I really understand what went on in class the day I missed."

**Situation 1:**   You were feeling confused and concerned about whether to stay in school or find a job. Your friend just spent three hours talking with you and helping you to resolve the problem.

**Your Compliment:**   _____

_____

_____

**Situation 2:**   While you were eating lunch with Margaret one day, she told you how much she enjoyed her trip to the coast with Betty. You've just run into Betty who begins to tell you about her weekend on the coast.

**Your Compliment:**   _____

_____

_____

**Situation 3:**   You've spent the last two hours eating lunch with a friend and you've really enjoyed talking with this person.

**Your Compliment:**   _____

_____

_____

**Situation 4:**   You're feeling troubled about a job interview that didn't go well. A friend calls you on the phone and after talking with this person for twenty minutes, you feel much happier, and far less concerned about the interview.

**Your Compliment:**   _____

_____

_____

\*From Glaser and Biglan, *Increase Your Confidence and Skill in Interpersonal Situations*, Chapter 5.

**Receiving
Compliments
Effectively:
Reinforcing the
Reinforcer**

What are some typical ways that people respond to compliments? Probably the most usual response is to deny (or in some way minimize) the compliment. Think for a moment about the impact this kind of receiving behavior can have on the communication climate. How would you feel, for example, if you say to a professor, "I want to tell you that I really enjoyed your lecture," and the reply is, "Gee, I thought it was terrible. I hardly prepared at all for it." Clearly, interpersonal climates can be negatively affected by rejection of compliment messages. But what are our alternatives? In this example, it would have been inappropriate for the professor to respond by saying, "Yes, I know. I'm a great teacher, aren't I?" How then, can we receive compliments so that the communication climate is enhanced and the sender made to feel valued for his or her contribution?

A simple "thanks" is almost always appropriate. Beyond that, we can enhance our reception of compliments by sharing with the other how the compliment makes us feel. In our example, the professor might have responded by saying, "Thank you for telling me that. I do work hard preparing my lectures and feel good when people find them stimulating." So we have three responses to compliments:

1. Thanks.
2. Thanks plus feeling ("I appreciate your telling me").
3. Thanks plus self-disclosure ("I worked hard on it").

The main point is this: the way we receive compliments does have a major influence on the communication climate we help to develop.

**Individual Activity
Receiving Compliments: Written Practice**

Listed below you will find a series of complimentary statements. Enhance the interpersonal climate by responding to each with one of the three types of compliment responses just discussed.

**1.** You are so disciplined. I'm impressed by how strict you are with yourself by coming to the library every night. _____

_____

_____

**2.** I really admire how you've stuck to your running program. You sure look fit. _____

_____

_____

**3.** I really do admire the way you play with your children. You seem to take them so seriously and have a good time with them too. _____

_____

_____

_____

**4.** You're really a good driver. I always feel comfortable and safe when I am a passenger in your car.

_____

_____

_____

**5.** What a great dinner. You are truly a gourmet cook. _____

_____

_____

_____

**Small Group Activity**
**Giving and Receiving Compliments**

Divide your class into groups of five or six people. Be sure each group arranges its chairs in a circle formation. Take three minutes to think of a compliment for the person sitting on your right. Then each person, in turn, delivers his or her compliment. The person receiving the compliment should respond in a way that acknowledges and accepts the sender's message.

After each compliment the other group participants discuss (a) what they liked best about the way the compliment was delivered and received; and (b) any changes they might suggest.

**Individual Activity**
**Giving Compliments In Actual Situations**

Choose a person whom you feel positively about and whom you see regularly. Over the next three or four days, keep a record of all the things this person does that pleases you or that you admire. You can also focus on physical appearance or possessions. Record this information on the form provided. Then, at the end of the four-day monitoring period, share one or more of your observations with the person involved. How did the person respond? How was the interpersonal climate influenced by your expressed appreciation of the other person?

| Situation | Appearance/Behavior I Found Pleasing or Admirable | Compliment I Might Have Given |
|---|---|---|
| | | |

## Provisionalism: Presenting Ideas Tentatively

Have you ever communicated with someone who had a dogmatic, know-it-all attitude? How did you feel when you talked with this person? How would you evaluate the communication climate in these situations?

When anyone presents ideas as if they were inflexible truths it helps to promote a negative communication climate. This is why, even if you feel strongly about an idea or position, it is important to acknowledge that another view may also be possible and worth listening to. Opinions are not absolute laws of nature. A question to ask yourself is: Does the wording of my message suggest finality rather than flexibility? If the answer to this is "yes," it would be useful to develop an alternative means of communicating the message.

Chapter 9 discussed how feelings and emotions can be more effectively communicated through the use of "I" language. This way of speaking has other benefits as well. Many people become irritated by judgmental "you" statements which they often interpret as indicating a lack of regard. "You talk too much," for example, is likely to provoke defensiveness and to have a negative impact on the communication climate. In contrast to "you" language (which is often evaluative and judgmental), descriptive "I" language puts the emphasis on the speaker. Instead of saying, "You talk too much," a descriptive communicator might say, "When you don't give me a chance to say what's on my mind, I feel frustrated."

## Group Activity
## Provisionalism: A Role-Play Demonstration

Choose two volunteers to enact the following scene between a parent and a college-age son or daughter.

**Situation:** It is two o'clock in the morning and the parent has been waiting up for the son or daughter who was expected home by midnight.

**Parent:** You feel angry and betrayed. You have asked your child to be home by midnight, a time you believe to be quite reasonable. Since going to college, your child has been losing respect for you. Your words no longer carry weight. You feel unfairly dealt with.

**Son or Daughter:** Your parent can't seem to recognize that you are in college now. You're still treated like a child although you feel like an adult. You can't understand why your parents refuse to grant you more freedom and responsibility to make your own life decisions. If your parents will not give you your freedom then you will just have to take it. And it looks like that's what it has come to.

**Instructions to Role Players:**  As you enact this situation, *do not attempt to be provisional* in your responses. Be as dogmatic and inflexible as the role may call for. After you have role played the situation once you will have another opportunity to reenact it in a more provisional way.

**Instructions to Class:**  As you observe this role play, take notes on dogmatic, inflexibly stated ideas. Present your observations in a class discussion immediately following the role play. Then make specific suggestions about how each of the role players might have responded in a more provisional manner. How might this have promoted a more positive communication climate?

After this discussion, role players will once again enact the scene, this time utilizing the suggestions for provisionalism offered by the class. At the conclusion of the second role play, consider the following questions: How did the communication climate differ between the first and second role play? What examples of provisionalism did you see? How did the tentative presentation of ideas affect each person's responses?

---

## Communication Climate: Receiving Input on the Impact of Your Own Behavior

The following questionnaire was developed to give you an opportunity to receive some direct feedback about the impact of your own behavior on communication climates.

Choose one to three people who know you and your communication fairly well. Ask each to fill out one of the Interpersonal Climate Questionnaires. Be sure they know that you will be the only person to see the results. Then, based on the information you receive, choose one to three behaviors to increase. For instance, you may choose to increase your frequency of responses to compliments, conversation maintainers, "I" language, or provisionalism.

## Interpersonal Climate Questionnaire

How frequently does the person you are rating engage in each of the behaviors listed below? For each behavior, rate the person on a scale from 1 to 7 where 1 signifies "extremely frequent" and 7 signifies "extremely rare." The person who gave you the questionnaire will be the only one to see the results. This is a self-improvement project and will not be used to evaluate the person in any way.

**1. Personal Attention:**  When I introduce a topic for discussion this person responds to my topic by asking questions, agreeing, disagreeing, or making other relevant comments.

| 1 | 2 | 3 | 4 | 5 | 6 | 7 |
|---|---|---|---|---|---|---|
| frequently | | | | | | rarely |

**2. Conversation Maintainers:**  When I talk this person encourages me by the use of content-free verbalizations such as: "hmmm"; "oh, I see"; "yes, go on."

| 1 | 2 | 3 | 4 | 5 | 6 | 7 |
|---|---|---|---|---|---|---|
| frequently | | | | | | rarely |

**3. Compliments:**  This person explicitly affirms the ways in which he or she appreciates me by telling me about specific behaviors of mine that are pleasing or admirable.

| 1 | 2 | 3 | 4 | 5 | 6 | 7 |
|---|---|---|---|---|---|---|
| frequently | | | | | | rarely |

**4. Receiving Compliments:**  When I compliment this person he or she responds by accepting the compliment and letting me know how good it felt to receive.

| 1 | 2 | 3 | 4 | 5 | 6 | 7 |
|---|---|---|---|---|---|---|
| frequently | | | | | | rarely |

**5. Provisionalism:**  This person presents ideas tentatively rather than inflexibly, acknowledging that other views are possible.

| 1 | 2 | 3 | 4 | 5 | 6 | 7 |
|---|---|---|---|---|---|---|
| frequently | | | | | | rarely |

**6. Nonaccusatory "I" Language:**  This person tends to describe rather than evaluate by behavior by phrasing talk in "I" rather than "you" language.

| 1 | 2 | 3 | 4 | 5 | 6 | 7 |
|---|---|---|---|---|---|---|
| frequently | | | | | | rarely |

## Requesting Behavior Change

Giving criticism in a way that is constructive for your friend and healthy for the relationship promotes a positive communication climate. Chapter 9 on emotions and Chapter 4 on language presented ideas for expressing your needs and problems in relationships. By combining a statement of your feelings with a specific behavior description, you will have an effective method of asking a friend to change behaviors with which you feel uncomfortable.

The system for asking for a behavior change includes a "STOP" phase, wherein you plan the interaction, and a "START" phase, in which you state your request. The entire planning and communication proceeds as follows:

### STOP

**1.** *Determine your outcome goal.* When you consider the goal, think about exactly what you want to have happen. EXAMPLE: I enjoy being with Mona, but I'm bothered by her cigarette smoke. I would like to do our visiting outdoors, where the smoke will blow away. I want to (1) continue to spend time with Mona, and (2) do outdoor activities like picnics, hikes, skiing, swimming, and running.

**2.** *Choose the best time.* When you learned about sharing feelings, you described some of the times that are good and bad for hearing about feelings. Considering that asking for a behavior change almost always involves sharing negative or problem feelings, what times would you predict to be poor choices for the interaction? Good times for the interaction?

**3.** *Edit the accusatory statements from your remarks.* You will want to avoid the sorts of inflammatory remarks that are likely to arouse defensive responses. Attacking statements, according to Chapter 10 of *Interplay,* tend to involve evaluation, control, manipulation, indifference, superiority, and certainty. Any such statements can damage the communication climate.

---

## Small Group Activity
### Accusatory Language

In groups of four or five people, brainstorm a list of statements that are accusatory. When the list is complete, think of alternative statements that would convey similar information in a supportive way.

| Accusatory Remark | Supportive Alternative |
|---|---|
| **EXAMPLE:** You're smoking too much. | When you smoke in the house I worry about whether I'm inhaling smoke too. |
| 1. | |
| 2. | |
| 3. | |
| 4. | |
| 5. | |
| 6. | |
| 7. | |
| 8. | |
| 9. | |
| 10. | |
| 11. | |

The "START" phase of requesting a behavior change consists of three steps that you learned in Chapter 4. These three steps accomplish the goal of accepting the responsibility for the request, as well as letting your partner know the details of the problem behavior and a preferred alternative. To review briefly, the three steps of the "START" phase are:

**START**

4. *Use "I" language plus a feeling statement.*

5. *Pinpoint and document the problem.*

6. *Give a preference statement telling your intention.*

**EXAMPLE:**

1. Goal: I want to spend time with Mona, but I don't want to be exposed to her cigarette smoke.

2. Time: when we're both relaxed, in the evening at my house.

3. Edit accusations: no blaming.

4. Language of responsibility. "I feel worried about inhaling smoke when you smoke in the house."

5. Pinpoint: "Especially, I'm concerned about being in this little dining room when you light up after dinner."

6. Preference: "Could we go outside on the porch, so we can both be comfortable when we talk?"

---

**Small Group Activity**
**Requesting Behavior Change: Role Play Practice**

Read each situation described below. Then, in groups of five to six people, develop a request for behavior change that you think would be effective in the situation. Take turns rehearsing each of these requests. To make it more challenging be sure the role player being asked to change behavior does not comply too easily.

**Situation 1:**   Your living partner consistently makes plans for dinner without consulting you.

**Situation 2:**   Your neighbor plays his electric guitar at an extremely high volume until after midnight. It keeps you awake almost every night.

**Situation 3:**   You and your roommate split the cost of groceries and share food. Recently, however, your roommate has been bringing guests over and feasting on your food supply.

**Situation 4:**   On many occasions your friend drops in unexpectedly without calling first. Since you often have other plans this behavior puts you in an uncomfortable position.

**Situation 5:**   Your living partner leaves dishes in the sink and clothes on the floor. Since you like a neat house, you are the one who ends up doing all the cleaning.

---

**Coping with Criticism**   It is difficult for many people to maintain a positive communication climate when confronted with critical remarks. Chapter 10 of *Interplay* presents a system for effectively coping with criticism. Let us briefly review the components of that system now.

1.   When criticized seek more information (question)

   a.   Ask for specifics

   b.   Guess about specifics

   c.   Paraphrase the speaker's ideas

   d.   Ask about the consequences of your behavior

   e.   Solicit additional complaints

2.   When criticized agree with the speaker

   a.   Agree with the truth

   b.   Agree with the odds

   c.   Agree in principle

   d.   Agree with the critic's perception

**Individual Activity**
**Coping with Criticism: Some Practice**

The following exercise* will help you to test your understanding of the procedure for coping with criticism. Below you will find a list of three complaints you may have heard before. For each one, indicate how you might use the questioning and agreeing techniques just described.

**EXAMPLE:**   "Sometimes I think you don't take me seriously. It seems like everything I say goes in one ear and out the other."

**EXAMPLE:**

1.  Questioning Responses:

    **a.**   Ask for specifics: "I'd understand what you mean better if you could give me some examples of when I seem to be ignoring you."

    **b.**   Guess about specifics: 'Are you talking about last week when I made dinner plans with the Smiths after you told me you didn't like them?"

    **c.**   Paraphase the speaker's ideas: "It sounds like you're mad at me because you think I'm just humoring you sometimes so you'll stop talking. Is that it?"

    **d.**   Ask about the consequences of your behavior: "What happens when I don't take you seriously?"

    **e.**   Solicit additional complaints: "Is it just my not taking you seriously that's upsetting you, or is there something else too?"

2.  Agreeing Responses:

    **a.**   Agree with the truth: "Well, I suppose you're right. Sometimes I don't pay attention to what you say, mostly when I'm tired or mad."

    **b.**   Agree with the odds: "I suppose you're probably right. I'm sure I don't always give you my full attention."

    **c.**   Agree in principle: "You're right. The decent thing would be for me to always pay attention to you. If I were a better communicator, I'd probably do it more."

    **d.**   Agree with the critic's perception: "I can see why you might think that I'm not listening when I say I'll do something and then don't."

*From Adler, *Confidence in Communication*, pp. 203-206.

**Statement A:** "You know, you're sure sensitive to criticism. You shouldn't be so touchy—it'll only get you in trouble."

1.  Questioning Responses:

    **a.** Ask for specifics: _____

    _____

    _____

    **b.** Guess about specifics: _____

    _____

    _____

    **c.** Paraphrase the speaker's ideas: _____

    _____

    _____

    **d.** Ask about the consequences of your behavior: _____

    _____

    _____

    **e.** Solicit additional complaints: _____

    _____

    _____

2.  Agreeing Responses:

    **a.** Agree with the truth: _____

    _____

    _____

    **b.** Agree with the odds: _____

    _____

    _____

    **c.** Agree in principle: _____

    _____

    _____

    **d.** Agree with the critic's perception: _____

    _____

    _____

**Statement B:**    "You're going to have to do a better job around here. I just don't think you're trying your hardest."

1.   Questioning Responses:

    **a.**   Ask for specifics: _____

    _____

    _____

    **b.**   Guess about specifics: _____

    _____

    _____

    **c.**   Paraphrase the speaker's ideas: _____

    _____

    _____

    **d.**   Ask about the consequences of your behavior: _____

    _____

    _____

    **e.**   Solicit additional complaints: _____

    _____

    _____

2.   Agreeing Responses:

    **a.**   Agree with the truth: _____

    _____

    _____

    **b.**   Agree with the odds: _____

    _____

    _____

    **c.**   Agree in principle: _____

    _____

    _____

    **d.**   Agree with the critic's perception: _____

    _____

    _____

**Statement C:** "You've certainly been in a lousy mood lately. Sometimes you're hard to live with."

**1.** Questioning Responses:

    **a.** Ask for specifics: _____

_____

_____

    **b.** Guess about specifics: _____

_____

_____

    **c.** Paraphrase the speaker's ideas: _____

_____

_____

    **d.** Ask about the consequences of your behavior: _____

_____

_____

    **e.** Solicit additional complaints: _____

_____

_____

**2.** Agreeing Responses:

    **a.** Agree with the truth: _____

_____

_____

    **b.** Agree with the odds: _____

_____

_____

    **c.** Agree in principle: _____

_____

_____

    **d.** Agree with the critic's perception: _____

_____

_____

## Small Group Activity
## Coping with Criticism: Some Role Playing

You will probably find it helpful to practice responding to criticism in a role play situation. You can do so by using any of the situations just given or generating some of your own. This procedure will give you an opportunity to make on-the-spot adaptations to your partner's message. Include observers in this exercise to provide feedback about the criticism-receiving strategies used and their probable effect on the communication climate.

# 11 Resolving Conflicts

When you live in a world where people have different tastes, beliefs, attitudes, habits, and needs, interpersonal conflict is bound to happen. You may have experienced conflict with a roommate who thinks the kitchen should be cleaned up right after a meal, whereas you feel sure that cleaning up the next morning is just fine. You may want to go to a science fiction film when your friend wants to see a mystery. In every ongoing relationship you experience decisions that must satisfy several people or questions that must be settled. Constructive conflict represents a systematic way to help reconcile differences. Differences left untouched can cause emotional distress and relational withdrawal. Differences handled thoughtlessly can cause destructive, unmanageable conflict. Therefore, rather than trying to avoid conflict altogether or jumping into nonproductive fights, you can focus on the process through which constructive change occurs.

You will learn in this chapter how to engage in conflict in such a way that relationships grow. You will develop ways of discussing specific issues with the idea of solving problems rather than just arguing. When you complete this chapter, you will have evaluated your current ideas and behaviors in conflict situations. In addition, you will practice and understand some specific skills for handling conflict more constructively.

**Individual Activity**
**Conflict Resolution: Assessing Your Style***

Think back over your recent history and recall five conflicts you have had. The more current, the better. The conflicts should be ones that occurred with people who are important to you, people with whom your relationship matters.

Using the form provided, describe the conflict, how you managed it, and the results. Based on your monitoring, answer the following questions.

**1.** Are you happy with the way you have handled your conflicts? Do you come away from them feeling better or worse than before?

**2.** Have your conflicts left your relationships stronger or weaker?

**3.** Do you recognize any patterns in your conflict style? For example, do you hold your angry feelings inside? Do you behave aggressively? Compliantly? Are you insulting? Sarcastic? Silent? Do you lose your temper easily?

**4.** Would you like to change the way you deal with your conflicts? How?

**1.  The Conflict**    (Describe who it was with, what it was about): _____

_____

_____

_____

_____

**How I Managed It:**    (What happened during the conflict? How did it end?) _____

_____

_____

_____

_____

**The Results:**    (How did you feel? How did the others involved feel? Are you happy with the results?)

_____

_____

_____

_____

*From Adler and Towne, *Looking Out/Looking In,* 4th ed.

**2.  The Conflict:** _____

_____

_____

_____

_____

**How I Managed It:** _____

_____

_____

_____

_____

**The Results:** _____

_____

_____

_____

_____

**3.  The Conflict:** _____

_____

_____

_____

_____

**How I Managed It:** _____

_____

_____

_____

_____

**The Results:** _____

_____

_____

_____

**4.  The Conflict:** _____

_____

_____

_____

_____

**How I Managed It:** _____

_____

_____

_____

_____

**The Results:** _____

_____

_____

_____

_____

**5.  The Conflict:** _____

_____

_____

_____

_____

**How I Managed It:** _____

_____

_____

_____

**The Results:** _____

_____

_____

_____

_____

## Assertive Communication

Chapter 11 of *Interplay* distinguishes four categories of conflict style. *Nonassertive* communicators yield their own needs to the needs of others; they accept unsatisfying conclusions. Although everyone occasionally opts for solutions they aren't pleased with, people may begin to act like martyrs if they overuse nonassertive communication. One nonassertive communicator called this problem "the doormat syndrome. I feel like everybody walks all over me."

*Indirectly aggressive* communicators express hostility in a concealed way. "Crazymaking" communication tries to masquerade as any number of more pleasant communication behaviors: humor, agreement, smoothing over. In indirect aggression, however, the person who receives the hostile message recognizes the intention, if not the immediate content, as aggressive. The duplicity of such hidden messages is more likely to produce discomfort than constructive work.

*Direct aggression* allows only one winner in conflict situations. People who overuse aggressive communication describe themselves as "one-up" or "one-down" in most relationship interactions. Inflexible aggression overwhelms opposition and, in the process, crushes the potential for creative interaction.

The ability to express regard for the needs and rights of others while standing up for your own rights and needs is *assertive communication*. Assertiveness combines the attitude "We can achieve satisfactory conflict resolution" with the skills needed to accomplish such a goal. Assertive communicators convey strength and equality by revealing their needs without infringing upon others.

We have already discussed several assertive skills: asking for behavior change (Chapters 9, 10), self-disclosing (Chapter 8), responding to criticism (Chapter 10), and using the language of responsibility (Chapters 4, 10). Another skill that is important in resolving feelings of conflict is learning to say "no." Saying "no" assertively allows both parties to manage time, resources, and the relationship bond most constructively. By deciding what you will and won't do in relationships, then expressing your decisions effectively, you can promote understanding of your constraints. When you say "no" constructively, you head off nonproductive arguing and your own resentment at being "trapped" into compliance. Your disclosure of constraints will set a climate in which your friends will be more likely to let you know their preferences. A mutual practice of assertively saying "no" when you genuinely are not willing to consent is a crucial part of constructive conflict.

Saying "no" involves five elements of verbal and nonverbal behavior.

**1.** Say "no" immediately, then provide a reason. Avoid "I shouldn't."
**EXAMPLE:** No, I can't go tonight. My chemistry test is tomorrow.

**2.** Offer interpersonal encouragement.
**EXAMPLE:** No, I can't go tonight. I appreciate the invitation and I hope you'll ask me again some time.

**3.** Suggest an alternative.
**EXAMPLE:** No, I don't want to see that movie. Would you like to get a pizza?

**4.** Educate the person to your time management system.
**EXAMPLE:** No, I won't be ready to study together tonight. I can be prepared by tomorrow night, though.

**5.** Use direct eye contact and a firm vocal pitch and volume. Avoid long pauses, fillers, and random movement.

You may choose to implement only two or three elements from the list, depending upon the request to which you are responding. Whichever combination you choose, be sure to include the nonverbal elements and the firm "no" immediately. You may also wish to say "no" proactively, that is, explain your constraints before the request is made. In a proactive "no", you will use the same elements, merely anticipating a request with which you don't want to comply. For example, if you know your roommate is going to fly home for the weekend and in the past she has consistently asked you for a ride to the airport, you can realistically anticipate that she plans to ask you later this week. If you have made other plans, you would want to tell her, "Mary, I won't be able to drive you to the airport this weekend because I'm driving home after class on Thursday. I wanted to let you know so that you could make other plans."

**Individual Activity**
**Learning To Say "No": Written Practice**

**Situation 1:** Your roommate wants to borrow your car to take some friends out to a bar. You don't want to lend it. Your response: _____

**Situation 2:** A woman comes to your door and wants to give you a religious tract. You'd rather not accept the offer. Your response: _____

**Situation 3:**   A person you have dated invites you over for "a romantic dinner." You like this person as a friend, but you're not interested in a romance. Your response: _____

_____

_____

**Situation 4:**   Your brother-in-law wants to borrow $50. You have the money, but don't want to lend it. Your response: _____

_____

_____

**Situation 5:**   A classmate wants to borrow your chemistry notes. You need them to study for the midterm. Your response: _____

_____

_____

**Small Group Activity**
**Dysfunctional Arguing**

Though few people are experts in conflict resolution strategies, most have had considerable first-hand experience in dysfunctional arguing—destructive conflict behavior that fails to solve the activating issue. Before looking at alternatives for constructive conflict resolution, let's explore some of the more typical methods involved in resolving interpersonal arguments.

**1.**   In groups of five or six people brainstorm a detailed list of destructive arguing behaviors. Name and describe patterns of ineffective arguing that you have seen people use to resolve conflict.

**2.**   Based on this list, your group will develop a role play scene that demonstrates the dysfunctional arguing behaviors. The nature of the central conflict in your role play is completely optional, and so are the number of participants and their relationship with each other. The primary purpose of the role play is to present a conflict situation that demonstrates the dysfunctional arguing behaviors your group described in Step 1 of this exercise.

**3.**   Each group then presents its role play to the class, which tries to identify and describe the dysfunctional arguing behaviors observed. In the large class debriefing of the role play activities, it is important that the class focus on *behaviors*. People should cite specific examples from a given role play to demonstrate a particular arguing pattern.

## Conflict Occurs over Definition of Relationship Rules

All messages exchanged in a relationship become part of a larger system of rules concerning who has the right to say what to whom and under what circumstances (Haley, 1963). Because every act of communication between relational partners either establishes, maintains, or negates a relationship rule, interpersonal conflict erupts over seemingly innocuous issues. Imagine, for instance, that a wife says to her husband, "Take out the garbage," and the husband angrily replies, "You take it out for once, and stop trying to control my life." Many people would say this couple was arguing over the garbage. It is possible, however, to contend that the husband and wife were arguing about a relationship rule: Does the wife have the right to order her husband to do a particular household task? In this example, the wife's command, "Take out the garbage," would have established her right to tell her husband what to do, to direct his behavior. By angrily refusing, the husband attempts to negate that relationship rule and to clarify his position: If his wife attempts to *order* him to behave, he will angrily refuse.

Every message has two components: content and relationship. The content level is obvious—it represents the informational segment of the message. But every message also says something about the relationship between sender and receiver, and conflict usually erupts over this relationship level. Consider the following example: You and your roommate have agreed that you are both responsible for tidying up and taking care of your own clothes and dishes. One day you are late for school and leave your dirty dishes in the sink, planning to wash them as soon as you return. When you get home from school, your roommate says, "You slob, you left all the dishes in the sink. Get in there and clean them before my friends arrive." Your immediate response to this situation is, "I'll wash them tonight. I don't have time now." You say this even though, on a rational, logical level you know and agree that your dishes are your responsibility. In this situation it is not the content of the message that bothers you but rather the relationship aspect. You are saying, in effect, "You cannot order me around. We do not have a relationship where you can tell me what to do." Relational partners often think they are arguing over the content of messages, when, in fact, they are arguing over the relationship rules being established.

---

### Individual Activity
### Identifying Content and Relationship Levels of Meaning: Self-Monitoring

Review the five conflicts you described in the conflict style assessment exercise on p. 215. Using either these conflicts or more recent ones, describe the messages exchanged in terms of content and relationship levels of meaning, and record this information on the following form.

| Conflict | Content or Informational Level | Relationship Level |
|---|---|---|
| **EXAMPLE:**<br><br>**Father:**  "Get up to your room and pick up your toys."<br><br>**Child:**  "No, I don't have to. You can't make me." | Father wants child to put away toys. | **Father:**  "I can order you around and tell you what to do when you're not behaving in a way that's acceptable to me."<br><br>**Child:**  "I don't have to obey when you get bossy. You can't order me around." |

| Conflict | Content or Informational Level | Relationship Level |
|---|---|---|
|  |  |  |

## Resolving Conflict: Talking about Talk

By now you are probably wondering about your options for resolving relational conflict. If so much of our arguing concerns implicit relationship rules rather than explicit content, how can conflict be functionally resolved? If an argument over garbage dumping or dirty dishes is actually about whether it is legitimate and permissible to demand behavior from a relational partner, then how can these interpersonal problems be solved?

In order to resolve conflict about relationship rules, we make our communication the topic of conversation; we talk about our talk. This process is called *metacommunication*. Imagine, for instance, that you are the berated roommate being directed to wash your dishes in the example discussed earlier. In this situation it would be appropriate and useful to metacommunicate, making your roommate's talk the content of your message. You might say, for example, "I know it is my responsibility to clean my own dishes and I had planned to. But when you call me a slob and *demand* that I do what you say, I feel defensive and I want to refuse. I feel you are saying that we have the kind of a relationship where you can give me directives, where you can order me around and expect me to obey. It's that I am resisting. I know that it is my obligation to wash my dishes and I agreed to that. What I can't agree to is your right to boss me around."

It would then be useful for you to offer your roommate alternatives and suggestions for sending his or her message in a manner that you would find more acceptable and less aversive. Much relational conflict can be resolved by making communication the topic of discussion.

## Class Discussion
## Metacommunication: A Role Play

Choose two volunteers from your class to enact the following role play. While the role play is being performed the class should take notes on the following questions: What relationship rules are being negotiated, argued about? In which situations is the relationship aspect of the message more salient than the content? Where does conflict erupt from relationship levels of meaning? What examples of metacommunication do you observe? Can you think of instances in which metacommunication could have been used to help resolve conflict?

**Flo:**   Sal is never home. If he is not working he is out playing poker. What kind of fool does he take you for? This isn't what you bargained for when you agreed to marriage. But now you are saddled with two kids and a transient husband that you see less than the gardener. Is he bored with you? Is he playing around? You don't know and you are at the end of your rope. Either he stays home more or you want out. Now is the time to set him straight.

**Sal:**   Flo has been such a pain lately, always whimpering and whining about something. Thank goodness that between staying late at the office and playing poker, you have been able to keep away six nights out of seven. Not that you don't appreciate Flo. She is a good mother and in her better moments a pretty good wife. But you don't like being smothered. When you agreed to this marriage, it was with the proviso that each would maintain some independence. Now seems like a good time to remind Flo of those earlier commitments.

## Resolving Conflict:
## Own Your Problem

A problem is yours when your needs are left unmet. Even though you may believe that your problem is generated by someone else's inconsiderateness, dishonesty, or selfishness, it is still your problem if you are left with unresolved needs. Acknowledging this problem ownership is an important aspect of conflict resolution, for when you present annoying, selfish, or inconsiderate behaviors of others as *your problem*, the likelihood of resolving the conflict is increased. People respond with less defensiveness and resistance when they are not being accused or attacked. According to Gordon (1970), a statement of problem ownership should contain three elements:

1.   A description of the specific behavior that presents a problem for you.
2.   An outline of the concrete, observable consequences of this problem.
3.   A description of the feelings you experience as a result of the problem.

Gordon developed a formula for presenting this information:
"I have a problem. When you _____ , then
                                    specific behavior

_____ happens, and I feel
    specific consequences
_____ ."
    your feelings

Imagine, for instance, that your neighbor keeps you awake by playing her stereo after midnight. Using Gordon's formula, you might describe your problem in the following way:

> "I have a problem. When you play your stereo this loud after midnight (behavior), I can't sleep and then I have a hard time waking up in the morning (consequences). I get really upset when this happens (feelings)."

Sometimes your message will make more sense if you rearrange the three central elements. The behavior that bothers you, its consequences, and your feelings do not have to be stated in any particular order. It is also possible to use words different from "I have a problem" to indicate problem ownership. The critical issue is that all these elements are present and communicated to the other person. The following example demonstrates the flexibility of the problem ownership structure.

Imagine that for some time you have felt that an old friend is angry with you. This person has not suggested that you get together for at least two months. And when you suggest a date, your friend usually finds a reason to refuse. Using a flexible problem ownership structure you might say to your friend, "There is something that has been bothering me and I want to talk with you about it (I have a problem). I'm afraid that you are angry with me for some reason (feelings). I say that because you haven't invited me to get together with you for more than two months. And when I suggest we get together, you say that you are busy (behavior). I'm worried that if things go on this way our friendship will be over and I would hate to see that (consequences)."

---

**Individual Activity**
**I Have a Problem: Written Practice**

Write an "I have a problem" response for each of the situations that follow. Remember to include in your answer a description of the specific behavior that represents your problem, the consequencs of that behavior, and a clear description of your feelings. Label each of these elements in parentheses.

**Situation 1:**   Your roommate from last year continues to drop by unannounced. Although you are very fond of this person and do wish to continue a relationship, he or she seems to find the most inopportune times to call on you. You are about to sit down and do some math homework when your doorbell rings. It's your roommate from last year.

**Your Statement:** _____

_____

_____

_____

_____

**Situation 2:**   Your neighbor's dog wakes you at 5:00 A.M. every morning by barking. To make it worse, the dog continues to bark until about 6:30 A.M. so you can't even get back to sleep. You decide to speak to your neighbor about the situation.

**Your Statement:** _____

_____

_____

_____

_____

   Once you have completed the statements and are satisfied that you understand how to use the "I have a problem" format, turn to the personal conflicts you described on p. 211. In the spaces below describe how you could apply this new method if you chose to share each of your problems with the person(s) involved. As before, be sure to clearly identify the problem as your own, and to describe the troublesome behavior, its consequences, and your resulting feelings.

**Conflict 1:** _____

_____

_____

_____

_____

**Conflict 2:** _____

_____

_____

_____

_____

**Conflict 3:** _____

_____

_____

_____

_____

**Conflict 4:** _____

_____

_____

_____

_____

**Conflict 5:** _____

_____

_____

_____

_____

**Resolving Conflict:
Interpersonal Problem
Solving**

This section presents a format for conflict resolution. Earlier, this chapter
made the point that most interpersonal arguing fails to focus on and resolve
the issue central to the conflict situation. For a conflict resolution strategy to
be effective it must solve the problem that initiated the conflict. The six-step
procedure presented below is designed to guide participants through a
functional resolution of the central issue involved in their interpersonal
conflict. Note that this problem solving format represents an organizational
framework which includes many of the specific skills discussed in earlier
chapters. Rather than presenting new skills, then, the procedure provides
you with a method of organizing and using skills you have already acquired
to resolve conflict more effectively.

**1. Clarify Intentions to Work on the Problem.** Before two people can
engage in meaningful problem solving, both must agree to the process.
Although describing emotions and feelings is a later step in the conflict
resolution procedure, cathartic self-expression is *not* problem solving. If you
or your partner want to vent emotions before engaging in structured
problem solving, that is legitimate. But you must recognize that structureless

self-expression does not usually lead to the resolution of interpersonal conflict. Timing is important in conflict resolution, and people are not usually receptive to problem solving when they are tired, emotionally drained, or particularly busy. Therefore, setting a date to work on conflict is appropriate, reasonable, and useful. Postponing an argument, however, is not the same as saying, "I don't want to talk about it." Postponing means literally setting a time, making an appointment, for engaging in problem solving. The main point is that before interpersonal problem solving can proceed, both you and your partner must agree to the process and be prepared to *work* on the issues.

**2.   Define the Problem.**   Before conflict can be resolved, you must clearly define the central problem—the major issues must be pinpointed, described, and agreed upon. A poorly defined problem is rarely resolved. In addition, both of you must be satisfied with the definition of a problem before it becomes a viable framework for conflict resolution. For example, if a couple is consistently fighting about childcare responsibilities, the definition of the problem is critical. It would probably not be acceptable to the husband for his wife to state the problem as: "How can I get my husband to spend more time with our child?" It would also probably not be acceptable to the wife for her husband to define the problem as: "How can I get my wife to stop complaining so much about my not spending enough time with our child?" A more appropriate problem definition might be: "How can we both manage our other responsibilities, have time for ourselves, and still be sure our daughter is effectively cared for?" This last problem definition would more likely be acceptable to both of the participants in this conflict situation.

It is often helpful for interpersonal problems to be defined as questions, and for the wording to be broad enough to encourage a wide range of possible solutions. Often when people are first learning to define interpersonal problems, their wording is so narrow that it excludes many options. One common mistake is to present a solution as if it were a problem statement. In the childcare situation above, for example, a restrictively narrow definition of the problem might be: Should we send our child to a daycare center? Although daycare is certainly one option to consider, defining the problem in such a manner discourages the couple from generating other possible solutions. The definition of an interpersonal problem, then, should be acceptable to both participants and stated broadly enough to encourage a wide range of possible solutions.

**3.   Explicitly Describe Feelings and Intentions about the Issue.**   Although it was mentioned earlier that cathartic self-expression is not problem solving, once the conflict has been defined, it is important that both you and your partner describe your feelings and intentions concerning the problem, using active listening to avoid misunderstanding. Each of you should have a clear understanding of how the other feels about the problem and what that person wants. The point here is that both people should understand, although not necessarily agree with, the other's feelings before proceeding with the problem solving process. You will use many of the communication skills discussed earlier in this book in this phase of problem solving: self responsible "I" statements, nonaccusatory language, pinpointing, feeling descriptions, intention descriptions, problem ownership, nonverbal attention, paraphrasing, perception checking. The important point is that both you and your relational partner should understand each other's feelings surrounding the problem. It is more difficult to be angry with feelings than with demands.

**4.   Suggest Solutions for the Problem.**   Have a brainstorming session in which both you and your partner suggest as many solutions for the problem as you can generate. *Quantity* not quality is the key to this segment of interpersonal problem solving. This is because it is easier to develop a solution from thirty ideas than from three. Ideas that at first appear to be outrageous or extreme can often be modified and then incorporated into the eventual solution. This means that no matter how wild the idea, it should be included. In the childcare situation, for example, "sending our child to live with her grandparents" is just as legitimate in the brainstorming phase as "sending our child to daycare." Ideas are neither discussed nor excluded in the brainstorming segment of problem solving.

**5.   Develop a Tentative Solution.**   Based on the suggestions generated in the brainstorming session, combine, delete, modify, revise and develop one tentative solution to try for a set period of time. The solution that you ultimately choose must be satisfactory to both of you. If not, it probably will not work. Remember, the selected solution can be a creative *combination* of ideas developed in the brainstorming session. You should view the solution as tentative and flexible rather than conclusive or terminal; it is being evaluated, but not finalized. If the solution turns out to be unacceptable to either of you, it is then important to develop a different solution or a modified alternative. This perspective reduces frustration and establishes conflict resolution as an ongoing process rather than a one-trial success/failure model.

**6.   Establish a Time to Meet Again.**   Decide on a specific time when you will meet again with your relational partner to discuss and evaluate your progress in solving your problem. Since many attempts at resolving conflict end in failure and fighting, this evaluation appointment is important. Agreeing in advance to assess the workability of the solution at a specified time allows you and your relational partner to alter and modify a particular solution before you allow it to fail. It also means that you are viewing conflict resolution as a continual process rather than a one-shot trial that either ends in success or failure. If one or both of you are concerned that you may find it difficult to comply with the solution, it is possible to establish a very short trial period before evaluating the solution's workability.

## Small Group Activity
## Interpersonal Problem Solving: An Application

Return to the groups you were in for the dysfunctional arguing role play at the beginning of this chapter. Review the conflict situation your group developed and make some judgments about how the conflict might be more functionally handled using the interpersonal problem solving procedure just described. Then, develop a role play that demonstrates the resolution of your group's conflict situation.

**Individual Activity**
**Modifying Conflict Behavior in an Ongoing Relationship**

The purpose of the following assignment is to give you the opportunity to observe, record, and change conflict behavior in a particular relationship. For the first five to seven days monitor the conflict behavior in your relationship with your partner's cooperation if possible. Using the form provided, record the conflict events as they actually occur. This recording means that you will be monitoring and describing the event that led up to the conflict, the actual conflict situation, and how the conflict was resolved.

After doing this for approximately seven days, make some specific conflict resolution goals. What would you like to be doing differently with regard to your conflict resolution behavior? After you have defined your conflict resolution goal, for the next five to seven days attempt to implement this goal. Record your results on the form provided for this purpose.

| Day; Time | Events Preceding Argument | Subject of Argument | Statement(s) That Started Argument | My Purpose in Arguing |
|---|---|---|---|---|
| **EXAMPLE:** Mon., Oct. 1 9:00 A.M. | I am dressing; I'm in a hurry to get to school. Partner is relaxing in bed. | Who should pick up ice cream. | **Me:** "If you take the car, you have to pick up the ice cream." **Partner:** "I really don't want to do that. It's such a drag." | To convince partner she should pick up the ice cream since she was using the car all day. |

| Partner's Purpose | My Arguing Behaviors | Partner's Arguing Behaviors | Method of Resolution | Events Following |
|---|---|---|---|---|
| To tell me she was unwilling to do what I was demanding. | I said, "This is a disgusting way to start the day. If you can't take the responsibility that goes with the car, then don't take the car." | She said, "I don't want to talk about it," and pulled the covers over her head. | I slammed the door and biked to school. | Partner bought ice cream while I was at school, but she was quiet and irritable when I got home. |

**Goal for Conflict Resolution:** _____

_____

_____

_____

_____

_____

_____

_____

_____

_____

_____

_____

_____

_____

_____

_____

_____

_____

_____

_____

_____

_____

_____

_____

_____

_____

_____

_____

_____

_____

_____

_____

_____

_____

_____

_____

_____

_____

_____

_____

_____

_____

_____

_____

_____

_____

_____

_____

_____

_____

_____

_____

_____

_____

_____

_____

_____

_____

## Modifying Conflict Behavior: A Record

Now implement your conflict resolution goal and record your results on the chart that follows.

| Day; Time | Events Preceding Argument | Subject of Argument | Statement(s) That Started Argument | My Purpose in Arguing |
|---|---|---|---|---|
|  |  |  |  |  |

| Partner's Purpose | My Arguing Behaviors | Partner's Arguing Behaviors | Method of Resolution | Events Following |
|---|---|---|---|---|
| | | | | |

## Evaluation of Progress

After you have implemented your target conflict behaviors for about two weeks, evaluate your process. Which of your behaviors particularly pleased you? Were there any situations in which you were dissatisfied with your approach to resolving conflict? What changes would you now like to make? Which conflict behaviors would you like to increase? Are there any behaviors you intend to decrease?

Remember that your patterns for resolving conflict have been developed over many years. Therefore, you should be neither surprised nor discouraged to find that changing your conflict behavior takes time. You can, however, make enormous modifications in the way you resolve conflict, and you will find that your continuing effort will pay off in the increased comfort and satisfaction you feel in improved relationships.

# References

Adler, Ronald. *Confidence in Communication: A Guide to Assertive and Social Skills*. New York: Holt, Rinehart and Winston, 1977.

Adler, R., L. Rosenfeld and R. Towne.*Looking Out/ Looking In*, 4th Ed. New York: Holt, Rinehart and Winston, 1984.

Barker, Larry L. *Listening Behavior*. Englewood Cliffs, New Jersey: Prentice Hall, 1971.

Becvar, Raphael J. *Skills For Effective Communication: A Guide to Building Relationships*. New York: John Wiley and Sons, Inc., 1974.

Berscheid, Ellen, and Elaine Walster. *Interpersonal Attraction*. Reading, Mass.: Addison-Wesley, 1969.

Birdwhistell, Ray L. *Kinesics and Context*. Philadelphia: University of Pennsylvania Press, 1970.

Bitzer, Lloyd F. "The Rhetorical Situation." *Philosophy and Rhetoric*, 1, 1968.

Combs, Arthur, and Donald Snygg. *Individual Behavior*. New York: Harper and Row, 1959.

Dohrenward, B. S. "Some Effects of Open and Closed Questions on Respondent's Answers." *Human Organization*, 24 (1965), pp. 175–184.

Dow, Michael G., Susan R. Glaser, and Anthony Biglan. "The Relevance of Specific Conversational Behaviors to Ratings of Social Skill." *Journal of Behavioral Assessment*, 3 (No. 3), 1981, pp. 233–242.

Frost, Joyce Hocker, and William W. Wilmot. *Interpersonal Conflict*. Dubuque, Iowa: Wm. C. Brown, 1978.

Gilbert, Shirley J., and Gale G. Whiteneck. "Toward a Multidimensional Approach to the Study of Self-Disclosure." *Human Communication Research*, 2, 1976.

Glaser, Peter A., and Susan R. Glaser, "Marital Communication: An Addition to the Interpersonal Communication Curriculum." Paper delivered to the Speech Communication Association, December, 1977.

Glaser, S. R., A. Biglan, and M. G. Dow. "Conversational Skills Instruction for Communication Apprehension and Avoidance: Evaluation of a Treatment Program." *Communication Research,* 10:4 (October, 1983), pp. 582–613.

Glaser, S. R., and D. A. Frank. "Rhetorical Criticism of Interpersonal Discourse: An Exploratory Study." *Communication Quarterly,* 30:4 (Fall 1982).

Glaser, Susan R. "Interpersonal Communication Instruction: A Behavioral Competency Approach." *Communication Education,* 32 (April, 1983), pp. 221–225.

Glaser, Susan R. "Oral Communication Apprehension and Avoidance: The Current Status of Treatment Research." *Communication Education,* 30 (October, 1981), pp. 321–341.

Glaser, Susan R., and Anthony Biglan. *Increase Your Confidence and Skill in Interpersonal Situations.* Eugene: University of Oregon Press, 1977.

Gordon, Thomas. *Parent Effectiveness Training.* New York: Peter H. Wyden, 1970.

Gottman, John M. *A Couple's Guide to Communication.* Champaign, Illinois: Research Press, 1976.

Haley, Jay. *Strategies of Psychotherapy.* New York: Grune and Stratton, 1963.

Hargie, Owen, Christine Saunders, and David Dickson. *Social Skills in Interpersonal Communication.* London: Billings and Sons, Limited, 1981.

Hart, Roderick P., and Don M. Burks. "Rhetorical Sensitivity and Social Interaction." *Speech Monographs,* 39, June, 1972.

Hart, Roderick P., William Eadie, and Robert Carlson. "Rhetorical Sensitivity and Communicative Competence." Paper delivered to the Speech Communication Association, December, 1975.

Hayakawa, S. I. *Language in Thought and Action.* New York: Harcourt Brace Jovanovich, 1964.

Hayakawa, S. I. *The Use and Misuse of Language.* Greenwich, Connecticut: Fawcett Books, 1962.

Homans, George G. *Social Behavior: Its Elementary Forms.* New York: Harcourt, Brace and World, 1961.

Kazdin, Alan. "Effects of Covert Modeling and Model Reinforcement on Assertive Behavior." *Journal of Abnormal Psychology,* 33 (No. 3), 1974.

Knapp, Mark L. *Nonverbal Communication in Human Interaction,* 2nd Ed. New York: Holt, Rinehart and Winston, 1977.

Leathers, Dale. *Nonverbal Communication Systems.* Boston: Allyn and Bacon, Inc., 1976.

Mager, Robert. *Goal Analysis.* Belmont, California: Fearon Publishing Co., 1972.

Mahoney, Michael J.,*Cognition and Behavior Modification.* Cambridge, Massachusetts: Ballinger Publishing Co., 1974.

Mahoney, Michael J., and Carl Thorsen. *Self-Control: Power to the Person.* Monterey, California: Brooks/Cole Publishing Co., 1974.

Mead, George Herbert. *Mind, Self and Society.* Chicago: University of Chicago Press, 1934.

Mehrabian, Albert. *Nonverbal Communication.* Chicago: Aldine-Atherton, 1972.

Miller, Sherod, Elam Nunnally, and Daniel Wackman. *Alive and Aware: Improving Communication in Relationships.* Minneapolis: Interpersonal Communication Programs, Inc., 1978.

Pearce, W. Barnett, and Stewart M. Sharp. "Self-Disclosing Communication." *Journal of Communication,* 23, 1973.

Phillips, Gerald M., personal communication with, 1972.

Phillips, Gerald M., and Nancy J. Metzger. *Intimate Communication.* Boston: Allyn and Bacon, Inc., 1976.

Phillips, Gerald M., and Nancy J. Metzger. "The Reticent Syndrome: Some Theoretical Considerations About Etiology and Treatment." *Speech Monographs,* 40, 1973.

Rabkin, Richard. *Inner and Outer Space.* New York: W. W. Norton, 1970.

Rogers, Carl. *Client Centered Therapy.* Boston: Houghton Mifflin, 1951.

Rosenfeld, Lawrence B. "Self-Disclosure Avoidance: Why Am I Afraid to Tell You Who I Am?" *Communication Monographs,* 46, 1979.

Watzlawick, Paul, Janet Beavin, and Don Jackson. *Pragmatics of Human Communication.* New York: W. W. Norton, 1967.

Weiss, Robert L., Hyman Hops, and Gerald R. Patterson. "A Framework for Conceptualizing Marital Conflict: A Technology for Altering It, Some Data for Evaluating It." *In* Leo A. Hamerlynck, Lee C. Handy, and Erick J. Mash (eds). *Behavior Change: Methodology, Concepts, and Practice.* Champaign, Illinois: Research Press Co., 1973.

Wills, T. A., R. L. Weiss, and G. R. Patterson. "A Behavioral Analysis of the Determinants of Marital Satisfaction." *Journal of Consulting and Clinical Psychology,* 42, 1974.

Zimbardo, Philip. *Shyness: What It Is, What to Do About It.* Reading, Massachusetts: Addison-Wesley, 1977.

# Index

---